Aleck Bell

Ingenious Boy

Illustrated by Frank Nicholas

Aleck Bell

Ingenious Boy

By Mabel Cleland Widdemer

 THE **BOBBS-MERRILL** COMPANY, INC.
A SUBSIDIARY OF HOWARD W. SAMS & CO., INC.
Publisher · INDIANAPOLIS · NEW YORK

LIBRARY OF CONGRESS CATALOG CARD NUMBER: 62-12698

PRINTED IN THE UNITED STATES OF AMERICA

For my niece
Marjorie Russell Fletcher
with love

Illustrations

Numerous smaller illustrations

Contents

Books by Mabel Cleland Widdemer

ALECK BELL: INGENIOUS BOY

DE WITT CLINTON: BOY BUILDER

HARRIET BEECHER STOWE: CONNECTICUT GIRL

JAMES MONROE: GOOD NEIGHBOR BOY

PETER STUYVESANT: BOY WITH WOODEN SHOES

WASHINGTON IRVING: BOY OF OLD NEW YORK

★ Aleck Bell

Ingenious Boy

Aleck picked them up and wiped them off with his mittens. He found the paper, too, and wrapped them up again as well as he could. His nose itched and his eyes smarted. He wanted to cry, but he kept back his sobs. He knew it would please the bully to see him cry.

The boy had caught Melville's arm and was twisting it. Melville's face was white with pain, but he wasn't crying either.

Aleck flew at the big boy. He started to kick him hard.

"Two against one!" shouted the bully.

"You're twice as big as either of us!" Aleck cried. "You stop hurting my brother!"

Suddenly the bully let go of Melville's arm. He caught Aleck by the coat collar and held him off at arm's length. Aleck's short legs couldn't reach him any more.

"You're a game little beggar!" the big boy said. "Now promise not to kick me and I'll walk the rest of the way with you and your brother. There's none in the alley who'll lay a hand on you if I'm with you."

"All right," Aleck said.

He and his brother followed the swaggering figure. Aleck saw that the boy's clothing were tattered. His shoes were full of holes so that mud sloshed in at every step. Suddenly Aleck was sorry for him. It would be dreadful to be poor and wear old clothes like that. He looked down at his own square-toed boots that kept out the wet. He pulled his scarlet tam lower.

They reached the end of the alley.

"Good-by, and thank you," Aleck said politely.

"Thanks? For what?" the big boy sneered. "For throwing your candles in the muck?"

"No. For taking us through the alley," Aleck explained. "Somebody might have chased us."

Suddenly he had an idea. "Would you like to come to my birthday party?" he asked.

14

"Who? Me?" the bully asked. "Are you crazy? What would I do at your birthday party anyhow?"

"We'd like to have you come," Aleck said politely. "Honestly we would."

The boy shook his head. "Be off now!" he commanded. "If you're ever here again and get into trouble, just mention my name. It's Jamie Dunlop. No one bothers my friends."

He slipped away into the shadows.

The boys ran the rest of the way home. Aleck went ahead and opened the heavy front door. A delicious smell met their noses as they stepped into the hall. Half a dozen dinners were being cooked on half a dozen stoves. The Bell family lived in an old-fashioned "flat-house." Two families shared each floor of the house.

"Everybody is having something different for supper," Aleck laughed as they climbed the winding stairs. He stopped at the first landing

and sniffed. "The McDonalds are having cab-
bage!" he announced. Then he sniffed again.
"The McLanes have a chicken!"

"And onions," Melville, behind him, said.

They climbed to the next floor. It was where
they lived, and across the hall Sandy Cunningham, Aleck's best friend, lived. When they
opened the door of their apartment the best smell
of all floated out. It was the odor of cake baking!
Aleck knew it was for his birthday. How glad he
was he had saved the candles!

They went directly to the kitchen. It was warm
and cozy, and smelled wonderful.

"Here are the candles," Aleck said. He put
the muddied package on the table.

"Good!" Mrs. Bell exclaimed. Then she asked,
"What ever happened to get them so dirty? Did
you drop them?"

Melville told her about their adventure in
Shinbone Alley.

"All's well that ends well," Mrs. Bell said. "But don't go there again."

"Nothing could happen to us if we did," Aleck said. "We're friends now of Jamie Dunlop. We don't have to worry."

"That's right," Mrs. Bell agreed. "Now, Aleck, tell me what color you want the icing on your cake to be."

"Pink!" Aleck answered without hesitating. That was his favorite color.

"Your grandfather's cake is pink, too." Mrs. Bell told him.

"I'm glad. I want mine the same color as Grandfather's," Aleck said.

He leaned against the table and watched her beat up the icing. "Mother," he asked, "are Grandfather and I twins?"

Mrs. Bell laughed. "Why, no, dear! What ever made you think so?"

"Well, we have the same name, Alexander

Bell, and we have the same birthday—and we like the same things," he explained.

"You and he have the same name and the same birthday," Mrs. Bell agreed. "But you were born on March 3, 1847, so you are seven years old today. He was born on March 3, 1790, so he'll be sixty-four. No, you're not twins. You would both have to be my children and the same age, too, to be twins."

The thought of the white-haired grandfather being his young mother's son made Aleck laugh. He thought it very funny. So did Melville. Mrs. Bell laughed because she liked to see the boys enjoy a good joke. Edward Charles, four and a half and the baby of the family, laughed, too. He laughed only because the others did, and not because he enjoyed the joke.

The warm kitchen, filled with laughter, was a pleasant place to come into after the rain and wind of the dark streets. Mr. Alexander Melville Bell, the boys' father, was glad to get home that evening.

"My, how good it smells in here!" he said. He sniffed as his sons had done.

"I've been baking all day for the party," Mrs. Bell told him. "Mrs. Cunningham helped me, or I'd never have been through."

"The Cunninghams are good neighbors," Mr. Bell agreed.

All this time Aleck kept his brown eyes fastened on a mysteriously wrapped parcel. His father had placed it on the kitchen shelf next to the hand-painted wooden clock.

"Yes, that's for you, Aleck." Mr. Bell laughed.

"Go and get dressed," Mrs. Bell told the boys. "The guests will be here before we are ready. Are you sure you know the wee poem you learned for a birthday gift for your grandfather, Aleck?"

"Yes, I know it," Aleck nodded. He recited it, to show her.

When he finished his father said proudly "Well done! Your grandfather will be pleased with the way you pronounce your words slowly and clearly. I am proud of you, too. You know how we dislike to hear people jumble words together. You know we teach people to speak carefully and clearly."

"Aleck has worked hard over his poem," Mrs. Bell said. "Hurry now and get dressed."

The boys went to their room. Melville lifted the large china pitcher that had pink roses painted on it. He poured some water in the wash bowl for his brother. The pitcher was too heavy for Aleck to lift.

Aleck stuck first one finger, then another, into the water. It was cold. His father had pumped it out of the well in the back yard that morning. It still had the feel of snow in it. When his hands grew used to it he soaped them well and washed them thoroughly. Melville helped him part his thick mop of black hair that always wanted to stand on end. At least it would stay flat until the party began.

Aleck waited for Melville to dress, too. Then they went down the narrow long hall to the front parlor. It was brightly lighted by gas, which sputtered in a central chandelier. All the chairs were pushed back against the wall. There was a white linen cloth on the table that held the pink-iced cakes. The room looked cheerful.

There was a knock on the front door, and guests began to arrive. Aleck stood beside his parents and helped to welcome the guests, because it was his birthday.

Everyone had remembered to bring him a present. Soon there was a pile of packages on the small table by the door. Aleck could scarcely keep his eyes off them. He tried to imagine what was in every mysterious parcel. None of them could be opened until his grandfather came and the candles were lighted on the birthday cakes.

It grew later and later, and Grandfather Bell didn't come. People began to look at their watches. They stole quick looks at the clock on the mantel. Mrs. Bell thought of all the good food she had cooked. She wondered if it would spoil before Grandfather arrived.

Then they heard a loud knock on the door. There he was! Grandmother Bell was right behind him. Their arms were filled with packages, and they were smiling. They had come all the way from London.

"The train was held up by a thick fog," Grandfather Bell explained. "We thought we'd never get here."

Everybody was glad to see them. Now the party could begin. Grandfather Bell and Grandmother Bell liked people. They had a way of making everyone feel at ease and happy.

The candles were lighted on the birthday cakes. The presents were given out. Aleck got many things he had wanted for a long while. Grandmother Bell gave him an old kitchen clock.

"You can take it apart and see how it works." She smiled. "If you can't get it together again, it won't matter."

Aleck thought that was a wonderful present.

He took his slice of cake and went to sit by his friend Sandy Cunningham. He told him about Shinbone Alley and Jamie Dunlop.

"I wish I'd been with you," Sandy said.

"I'll take you there tomorrow. You can meet Jamie, too," Aleck promised.

He went back for a second helping of cake. He noticed a strange man and woman among the guests. They had a little girl with them. Aleck went over to speak to them politely.

"Hello," he said to the little girl. "I hope you are having a nice time."

She only looked at him and smiled. Aleck thought she was shy. She was a pretty little girl with big brown eyes and chestnut curls. When she smiled there was a dimple in her right cheek. Aleck watched her with other guests. She only smiled at them, too. She never spoke.

He went over to his mother. "Why doesn't that girl talk?" he asked. "She just smiles at everyone who speaks to her."

"Mary Ellen is deaf," Mrs. Bell explained. "She can't hear you, so she doesn't know what

24

words sound like. Your father is trying to teach her how to talk."

"Oh, he can teach her to talk, all right," Aleck said. "You know he has made all those pictures of the way your tongue and teeth look when you say some words, and the way your lips look when they make different letters. He'll soon teach her. You wait and see."

Mrs. Bell smiled. "Why, Aleck, I didn't know you were old enough to understand those symbols your father has drawn. He calls them 'Visible Speech,' you know."

Aleck nodded. "I know some of the pictures," he said proudly. "They were pretty easy to learn. Easier than A B C's." He sighed, for he had just learned the alphabet. "Do you suppose I could help Father teach Mary Ellen?" he asked eagerly. "I could help her."

"That would be very nice," Mrs. Bell smiled.

"It must be horrid not to be able to hear,"

Aleck said. "I think sound is the nicest thing in the world."

Someone was calling his name: "Aleck! Aleck!" He ran to see who it was.

"It's time for you to give your grandfather his birthday present," Mr. Bell whispered.

Aleck walked to the center of the room. The big pink roses in the carpet seemed to grow bigger as he stared shyly down at them. But if he looked up and caught Sandy's bright blue eyes he would laugh. The words of the little poem stuck in his throat. He thought, "I'll never be able to say them!"

"Come, come!" said his father impatiently. "Please begin, Aleck!"

He lifted his brown eyes to his father's face. He felt very young and small. He was scared.

Then little Mary Ellen laughed. He turned and looked at her. She was sitting on her mother's lap. She waved her hand.

Suddenly Aleck felt ashamed of himself. How terrible it would be not to be able to hear or speak! How lucky he was! How wrong it was for him not to open his mouth and recite the poem for his grandfather! He drew in a deep breath and began to speak:

"How doth the little busy bee
    Improve each shining hour,
And gather honey all the day
    From every opening flower. . . ."

Lost

ALECK didn't take Sandy to meet Jamie Dunlop after all. Mrs. Bell didn't want him to go back to Shinbone Alley. "Jamie Dunlop might not be there," she pointed out.

Aleck hadn't thought of that. "We'll go for a walk anyway," he told Sandy.

So they started out. They walked and walked. Once in a while they stopped and played a game of tag. Then they walked some more. It was a beautiful day. They didn't know it, but they walked clear to the edge of the city of Edinburgh. They went so far that the streets turned into country roads.

They met a farmer with an empty cart. He had been to market.

"Want a ride?" he asked.

"Oh, yes!" the boys cried. They climbed up beside him. They drove and drove. The farmer let them take turns holding the reins. They both enjoyed driving the big brown horses.

"I turn off here," the farmer said after a while. "Good-by, boys."

The boys scrambled down from the cart. They waved until the farmer was out of sight.

"I think we ought to go home," Aleck said. "It feels late."

"How do we get home?" Sandy asked. He didn't know where he was. He was scared.

Aleck spoke up bravely even though he was scared, too. "We'll walk back along the road we came on," he said.

They started. They hadn't noticed how many twists and turns and forks the road had. They had been too busy driving the horses. Finally they came to a little path.

"We'll follow this," Aleck said. "Maybe it will lead to a house."

They followed the path. It went on and on. Aleck felt he couldn't take another step. He wanted to lie down and take a nap, but he knew he mustn't do that. It was getting late. He must take Sandy home.

They went on and on. It began to grow dark. Sandy said, "I'm going to cry!" And he did.

Aleck didn't cry. They couldn't both cry. They'd never find their way home that way.

At last he saw a light through the trees. How friendly it looked! How glad he was to see it!

They came to a small white cottage in a clearing. Light was shining from the window.

They went to the front door. Aleck knocked. A dog barked loudly. Sandy grabbed Aleck's hand. Suppose only the dog was home?

Then the door was opened by an old lady in a white cap. She had the kindest face the boys had ever seen.

"What have we here?" she asked. She held out a friendly hand. "Come in, come in, my wee ones. You're just in time for supper."

She closed the door. Aleck and Sandy had walked right into her living room. There was a big fireplace at one end of the room. A black pot was hanging on a crane over the fire. A delicious smell came from the pot. The boys hadn't realized quite how hungry they were until they sniffed it!

A tall old man came out of the shadows. He wore a shepherd's plaid flung over one shoulder. On his feet were thick-soled boots. He still wore a black tam-o'-shanter on his white hair. He had just come home from tending his flock of sheep. He was tired and hungry, too.

He greeted the boys as kindly as his wife.

"Come close to the fire," he said. "There's plenty for all."

"Indeed and there's more than plenty," the old woman said. She bustled around putting two extra blue bowls on the table and two pewter spoons. She filled two mugs with milk. She pulled up a bench for the boys to sit on.

The big collie that had barked when they knocked on the door came to make friends with them. He nuzzled his nose into Aleck's hand. Aleck patted his head. He loved dogs.

"Help yourselves to the porridge," the old lady said. She placed a great steaming bowl of it on the table.

The boys ate a lot. Nobody asked any questions until they were through eating.

"Now, where do you live?" the old lady asked, after she had cleared the table.

"We live in Edinburgh," Aleck answered. "On Hope Street."

The old lady stared at them. She could scarcely believe her ears! They were miles and miles from home!

"How did you ever get way out here in the country?" she asked.

They told her about the farmer and how he had let them take turns driving the fat brown horses along the road.

"You poor wee ones!" she said. "Well, there's a bed for each of you. You'll spend the night with us. Tomorrow we'll take you home."

Aleck shook his dark head. "Our mothers will worry if we don't go home," he said. "They don't know where we are."

"Edinburgh is many miles from here," said the old lady. "You couldn't walk that far tonight. We have no way to carry you."

Aleck looked at the little old lady and at the tall old man. He wanted nothing more than to stay with them in their snug little house. He

wanted to get into a nice warm bed and wake up in the morning when the sun was shining and he wouldn't be so tired or sleepy. However, he knew his mother and Sandy's mother would be worrying about them. He said again, "We must go home."

"Douglas," said the little old woman suddenly, "there's nothing to do but that you should walk to Edinburgh. Tell the boys' parents what has happened. Tell them we'll see the boys get home safely in the morning. We can send them along to Edinburgh in the mail cart."

The old Scotch shepherd put on his tam-o'-shanter and wrapped his plaid around him. He picked up a lantern and a heavy walking stick. He whistled for his collie and started out.

Soon Aleck and Sandy were in bed. Aleck lay in the darkness thinking. It was the first time in his life that he had been unable to say good-night to his family.

"I wish," he said to himself, "that I could hear their voices, even if I couldn't see them. It would be nice if there was some way people could talk to other people at any time of the day or night, even if they were miles and miles apart. I wonder——"

He fell asleep thinking about it.

He Shall Have Music

ALECK sat in the corner of the horsehair-covered sofa. He was listening to his mother play the piano. Her fingers flew over the black and white keys. Ever since he was very small he had liked to listen to her play. He watched her fingers carefully. He listened closely.

"I'm sure I can play the piano," he thought. "I'm going to try."

Sandy called for him then. Aleck went off to play ball. He forgot all about playing the piano.

That afternoon it rained. Nobody wanted to stay outdoors.

"You can come to my house," Aleck told

Sandy. "We'll play some good games with Melville and Edward Charles."

"All right," Sandy agreed.

Just then Aleck saw a shabby figure walking up the street ahead of them. It seemed familiar. He hurried to catch up with the boy. It was Jamie Dunlop.

"Hello, Jamie!" Aleck cried. "Were you coming to see me?"

Jamie stared at Aleck. Then he grinned.

"You're the little beggar that kicked me," he said. "You've grown. Why should I be coming to see you? I don't know where you live. I don't even know your name."

Aleck laughed. "That's right! Well, I live just across the street in Number 13. Will you come and meet my mother?"

"She wouldn't want the likes of me in her house," Jamie said.

"Oh, she knows all about you. I told her you

38

were our friend. She'll be glad to meet you," Aleck said.

Jamie followed slowly. He didn't think Mrs. Bell would really like to meet him.

"Mother!" Aleck called when he opened the door. "Here's Jamie Dunlop come to call."

Mrs. Bell wasn't at home. She had gone to a concert with Mr. Bell.

Melville and Little Edward Charles raced down the long hall when they heard Aleck.

"Look, Melville," Aleck said. "Here's Jamie Dunlop. He's come to see us."

Melville looked surprised. "Hello, Jamie," he said. He didn't sound as if he was really glad to see Jamie.

"Hello," Jamie said gruffly.

So far Sandy had been quiet. Now he said, "Aleck has told me about you, Jamie. May I say I'm your friend, too, if I ever go through Shinbone Alley?"

"I guess so," Jamie said gruffly. He had never been in such a nice home as the Bells'. He felt shy and uncomfortable. It made his voice sound deep and grumpy.

"If you'll wipe your feet on the door mat we can go into the parlor," Aleck told Jamie. He took the big boy's tattered cap and put it on the table in the hall, next to a pretty silver basket. Mrs. Bell was very fond of that basket. It had been a wedding present.

Melville saw Jamie's small dark eyes dart toward the basket. He saw a strange, almost hungry look come into them. Melville was suddenly uneasy. Jamie had snatched the package of birthday candles out of his hand. After all, he lived in Shinbone Alley. What if he should steal the silver basket? Or anything else?

Melville caught Aleck's arm and pulled him into the kitchen. "You shouldn't have brought Jamie here. He may steal something!"

40

Aleck stared at his brother. He was surprised at him. Why, Jamie Dunlop was their friend.

"He won't take anything from a friend," he said stoutly.

"Well, we'd better watch him," Melville said.

Jamie had followed the other boys into the parlor. He looked around and blinked. He had never seen such a pretty room. He looked at the pale green carpet with the pink roses. He looked at the pale green draperies. There were paintings in gold frames on the walls. Every table seemed to be covered with wonderful things. He looked at a hand-painted snuffbox. How easy it would be to slip in into his pocket when no one was looking! He looked at a little slipper made of finely spun copper wire. That would bring a pretty penny!

Aleck and Melville came in.

"I will play the piano for you," Aleck announced grandly.

"Oh, you can't play the piano!" Sandy jeered. "You've never taken a lesson in your life!"

"You know you can't play," Melville said. "Besides, Mother wouldn't like you to touch her piano. She is very particular about her things." He spoke stiffly. He hoped Jamie Dunlop would take the hint and not try to touch anything in the room.

"I can so play!" Aleck cried. "You wait and see! Besides, I won't do anything to hurt Mother's piano."

He twirled up the red-velvet-covered stool. He sat down and raised his hands above the keys.

The boys stood watching him. Their mouths were open in amazement. They would never have dared to touch the rosewood piano.

Music was open on the rack before Aleck, but he didn't know one note from another. He knew only the tunes his mother played. They were all there inside his head.

He brought his hands down on the keys as he had seen Mrs. Bell do. Then he began to play, slowly at first. He gained confidence when the notes sounded the way they did when his mother played. He played "Annie Laurie" straight through. Then he twirled around on the piano stool and shouted triumphantly, "I told you I could play the piano!"

The boys stared at him. They couldn't believe their ears. Why, to play the piano you had to take lessons and practice for hours and hours! Here was Aleck playing "Annie Laurie" the first time he ever sat down at the piano!

"If you can do it, I can do it!" Sandy said.

Then they all wanted to try. They pushed and shoved one another. Even Jamie took a turn. But none of them could play. They just made loud, unpleasant noises.

"How do you do it, Aleck?" Melville asked. "Play something else and let us watch you."

"I'll play 'Home Sweet Home,'" Aleck said, and he did.

None of them heard the front door open and close. None of them knew that Mr. and Mrs. Bell had returned, bringing a guest. None of them heard anything until Aleck finished his piece and twirled around again on the stool.

"Bravo!" said a voice from the doorway. "That was fine!"

Aleck jumped off the stool. He looked shyly at the stranger who was with his parents. His mother would probably scold him for touching her piano and for bringing the boys into the parlor. He hoped she wouldn't scold him too much in front of the tall dark man.

But she was smiling. "Why, Aleck, I didn't know you could play the piano!" she said delightedly. "That was very nice."

"I didn't know either," Aleck answered, "until I tried!"

The strange dark gentleman exclaimed, "Do you mean the boy has never had a lesson?"

He was surprised. He taught people how to play the piano. He was very famous. He gave concerts where he played before hundreds of people. The Bells had been to his concert that afternoon. They had brought him home to tea.

"No, Signor Bertini, Aleck has never had a lesson," Mrs. Bell said.

"I have never heard anything like it," Signor Auguste Benoit Bertini exclaimed. "The boy has a perfect ear. He is a natural-born musician. I shall give him lessons." He added proudly, "He shall become a famous musician like me! How would you like that, my boy?"

Aleck didn't say anything. Mrs. Bell was delighted, but Mr. Bell was silent. He wasn't sure he wanted Aleck to be a musician.

Signor Bertini patted Aleck's head. "Come to my house tomorrow for your first lesson," he said.

"I will," Aleck promised. He thanked Signor Bertini politely.

"Someday the name of Alexander Bell will be outside many concert halls," Signor Bertini said. "I shall help to put it there."

Aleck laughed. "Nobody will know if it's Grandfather or Father or me!" he said. "We all have the same name."

Mrs. Bell went out to get the tea. Aleck followed her.

"I want you to meet Jamie Dunlop, Mother," he said. "May I bring him out here to the kitchen for a minute?"

"Where is he, Aleck?" Mr. Bell asked. "I didn't see him in the parlor with the other boys when we came home."

Aleck looked surprised. "Why, he must be there, Mother! He was there while I was playing the piano. He even tried to play himself."

He hurried back to the parlor to see. His

mother was right. Jamie wasn't in the parlor. He wasn't in the hall. He wasn't anywhere. Aleck looked for Jamie's ragged cap on the table in the hall.

It was gone. So was Mrs. Bell's wedding present, the little silver basket that she liked so well!

A Name of His Own

ALECK was very, very angry. He had trusted Jamie Dunlop, even though Melville had warned him. He had thought Jamie was a friend. You didn't steal from friends.

He went to his room and got his tam and coat. He took his china bank with him. It was shaped like a pig. He had been saving his shillings and pennies for a long time. The bank was so full it didn't even make a noise any more when he shook it. He slipped out of the house quietly.

"I'll go to Shinbone Alley and find Jamie. I'll make him give me back the basket," Aleck said to himself.

He ran and ran. It had grown colder. The rain had turned to sleet and snow. If Aleck hurried he might get home in time for supper. He couldn't face his family until he got the basket back. His mother would feel sad when she learned it had been stolen. Melville wouldn't say, "I told you so"—he was too nice a brother to do that. But Aleck knew he could say it if he wanted to. Melville had warned him.

How dark and cold it was in Shinbone Alley! How smelly! What a horrid place to live! Aleck began to feel sorry for Jamie, but he felt even sorrier for his mother. She liked her silver basket very much. Jamie had no right to take it.

Aleck remembered the arched doorway out of which Jamie had stepped that afternoon to snatch at the birthday candles. It had been a long time ago, but the alley hadn't changed.

He knocked on an unpainted wooden door. A big man opened it.

50

"What do you want?" he demanded.

"I want to see Jamie Dunlop," Aleck answered. He tried to keep his voice steady, but he was shaking in his boots. The man was rough and evil-looking.

"Who are you?" he growled.

"A friend of Jamie's," Aleck said.

The man looked surprised. "A friend of Jamie's! You!" he exclaimed. He stared at Aleck's neat coat and his strong, well-made shoes and his tam.

"Yes, sir. Is he at home?" Aleck kept well away from the man. He was afraid he would grab him suddenly.

"Jamie is down at Mother Saunders' place," the man said.

"Where does she live?" Aleck asked. "How can I get there?"

"What do you want to know for? Why do you want to see him?"

"He has something that belongs to me and I've come to get it," Aleck said bravely.

He was sorry the moment he had spoken. The man brought his thick brows together. He reached out a long arm and caught Aleck's collar. Aleck tried to struggle free, but he couldn't. The man held on tightly.

"You're a sneaking little snooper!" the man growled. "Trying to get me to tell you where Mother Saunders is. Saying Jamie has something of yours."

"He's got my mother's silver basket," Aleck said. "He came to my house this afternoon and took it. I want it back."

"A fine story!" the man sneered. "You're a little sneak and liar!" He shook Aleck until his teeth chattered.

"You let me alone!" Aleck shouted. "Jamie told me if I said I was his friend no one in Shinbone Alley would touch me."

"He's not your friend! You just called him a thief!" The man shook Aleck harder than ever.

"Stop it!" Aleck cried. "You're hurting me! I'm not mad at Jamie for taking the basket. I'm sorry for him. It must be awful to be poor and live here. It must be awful to wear broken shoes and ragged clothes, and not have enough to eat. If the basket was mine, he could keep it forever, but it's my mother's. She likes it because it was a wedding present. That's why I want Jamie to give it back."

The man loosened his hold on Aleck. "You sound as if you were speaking the truth," he said.

"I am," Aleck said. "I guess Jamie needed some money or he wouldn't have taken the basket. I've brought my bank with me. I've stuffed it full. He's welcome to it."

"Here's your basket," Jamie said from behind. "I'm sorry I took it, but it was so handy to my cap. My ma is sick, and I thought if I sold it I could buy her some medicine or maybe get a doctor. Mother Saunders wouldn't buy it, though. She was afraid she'd get into trouble."

Aleck took the basket and thrust his bank into Jamie's hand.

"Take this," he said. "Here's money enough for a doctor and medicine, too. I've been saving for ever so long. If you tell me where you live I'll ask my mother to come around tomorrow. She'll bring you a basket of good things. She'll help your mother. She and other ladies in her church visit sick people. She'll know just what to do."

"No. She'd put me in jail if she saw me," said Jamie suspiciously.

"Oh, no, she won't!" Aleck said indignantly. "She'd feel sorry your mother's sick. She'd understand why you took the basket. I'll tell her everything when I get home."

"He seems to be speaking the truth, Jamie," the rough man said, suddenly siding with Aleck.

54

"Why don't you take a chance? Your Ma does need help."

"All right," Jamie said gruffly. He told Aleck where he lived.

"My mother will come tomorrow," Aleck promised. "And thank you for the basket."

"You're a queer one. Always thanking people for funny things," Jamie said.

He walked to the end of the alley and saw Aleck safely on his way. It was snowing hard now. Aleck ran through the storm. The collar of his tweed coat was pulled high around his ears. His red tam was pulled down almost to his nose.

Edinburgh looked pretty in the snowstorm. The old castle on the hill, where many Kings and Queens of Scotland had lived, looked like something in a fairy tale.

When he reached home and opened the door a delicious smell of baking ham came to his nostrils. It came from his mother's kitchen.

"Somebody is coming to supper," he thought as he climbed the stairs. Baked ham always meant "company" in the Bell household.

Aleck stopped a moment in the dim hall and placed the basket carefully on the table. He wondered if his mother had missed it. Perhaps she had been too busy getting ready for the guests to have noticed. He hoped so.

He stopped at the kitchen door. Mrs. Bell was just taking the ham out of the oven. It was beautifully browned and cloves were stuck in it. Aleck felt his mouth water. The ham smelled even better when he was close to it.

"Who's in the parlor?" he asked.

"Mr. Alexander Graham, a friend of your father's," Mrs. Bell answered. She put the ham on a large platter.

"Another Alexander!" Aleck said.

His mother laughed. "That is a good Scotch name," she told him.

56

"I'd like a name of my own," Aleck said. "When I grow up nobody will be able to tell me from Father or Grandfather. People say I even look like Grandfather."

"Oh, people will be able to tell you apart," Mother said with a smile. "He'll always be fifty-seven years older than you, remember."

That didn't satisfy Aleck. He still wanted his own name.

"Now run to your room and get ready for supper," Mrs. Bell said.

Aleck hurried. He was anxious to meet his father's friend. Mr. Alexander Graham was a tall, blond man with the bluest eyes Aleck had ever seen. He had a big yellow mustache, too.

"I live in Cuba," he told Aleck. "I have a plantation there. I've come back to visit old friends here in Scotland."

Aleck didn't know much about Cuba. He wished Mr. Graham would tell him something about it. It sounded nice. Aleck wished he were in a warm place on a night like this. It was snowing now harder than ever.

When supper was over, the Bell family went back to the parlor. It was cozy and warm there. Aleck could imagine how the wind must be howling through Shinbone Alley. He thought of his friends, the McGregors, in the small white house where he and Sandy had spent the night. He wondered if anyone could tell it from a snowbank on a night like this.

Mrs. Bell looked at the clock on the mantel. "Time for bed," she said to young Edward Charles. He could hardly keep his eyes open.

Aleck made himself as small as possible. He hoped his mother wouldn't send him off to bed, too. He wanted to hear Mr. Graham tell about his sugar plantation in Cuba. He like to hear about new lands. Someday he meant to travel.

"The island of Cuba is long and narrow. It is

somewhat the shape of an uneven crescent," Mr. Graham began.

Aleck crept closer to Mr. Graham's chair so he wouldn't miss a word.

"In the west there are swelling hills and gentle valleys," Mr. Graham continued. "The royal

59

palm is the commonest kind of tree to be seen there. There are many bright-colored flowers. You'd like them, Mrs. Bell." Mr. Graham smiled at his hostess. "We have two seasons in Cuba," he went on. "The dry season is from November to April. There is a hotter wet season from April back to November."

Aleck and Melville listened to Mr. Graham's tales of his travels back and forth to Cuba. He told of the storms he had been in at sea, and of his home on a sugar plantation. Aleck admired his stories very much. He thought Mr. Graham was the nicest visitor his father and mother had ever entertained.

At last it was time for Mr. Graham to leave. Mr. Bell said he must have some good strong hot tea before he set out into the snowstorm. Mrs. Bell agreed and went out to the kitchen to prepare it.

"Aleck Bell!" she cried, when he slipped out to

60

help her in the kitchen. "I thought you'd gone to bed hours ago."

"Oh, no, Mother, and please don't make me go now. I like to listen to Mr. Graham's stories. Wasn't he smart to think of hammering on a hollow tree trunk and spelling out words that way, so his helper wouldn't have to leave what he was doing and come all the way to talk to him? I'd like to think up a way for people to talk to one another across miles and miles of land."

"That would be wonderful." Mrs. Bell smiled. "You're right. Mr. Graham is a clever man. I like to listen to his stories, too. You may stay up until he goes."

So Aleck and Melville each had a glass of hot milk to drink while the grownups sipped their strong tea.

All of a sudden Aleck jumped to his feet.

"I'm going to call myself Alexander *Graham* Bell from now on!" he announced excitedly.

"That will be my own name. Nobody will have one like it."

"Well, well, that would be very nice," Mr. Graham said, flushing. He was pleased, but he didn't know how Mr. and Mrs. Bell would feel about their son taking his name.

"I think it's an excellent idea," Mrs. Bell cried. "Aleck has been wanting a name of his own for a long time."

"So do I!" Mr. Bell agreed. "Come, we'll make this a christening party. We'll drink to Aleck's new name."

Mr. Graham and Mr. and Mrs. Bell stood and raised their cups. Melville stood up, too, and raised his glass.

"To Alexander Graham Bell!" Mr. Bell said.

"Yes, here's to Alexander Graham Bell!" everyone echoed.

"To my very own name!" Aleck said to himself, and drank his milk.

Aleck had a lot to think about when he went to bed that night. First of all, he must remember to ask his mother to visit Jamie Dunlop's mother and take her a basket of good things. Then he could hardly wait to see Sandy tomorrow and tell him about his new name.

"I'll get him to call me Graham," he thought. "Then I'll really have a name of my own."

A Sad Discovery

IT WAS spring again. Aleck's birthday had come and gone. The April air was scented with growing things.

One day Mr. Bell drove his sons out to visit old Mr. and Mrs. McGregor. Mrs. McGregor's big gray cat had a family of six kittens. The collie, Duffer, was the proud father of a litter of puppies. There were a dozen new lambs in Mr. McGregor's flock of sheep.

Aleck and Melville grew restless after a while. The little farm was nice, but they had seen all there was to see. They wanted to go for a walk.

Mrs. McGregor laughed. "Stop shuffling your

feet, boys," she said, "and get up on them! Go out and take a walk. There's a robin's nest in the hawthorne tree down by the brook. You might see an egg or two. But you mustn't frighten the mother bird. She might fly away and leave her nest and never return to it. Then none of the eggs would be hatched."

The boys ran out. How good everything smelled. They took deep breaths as they ran across the fields and meadows. They felt like running as fast as they could.

When they drew near the hawthorne tree by the wild little brook that rushed over and around brown stones, they walked as quietly as their thick-soled boots would allow them. They didn't want to frighten the mother bird.

They tiptoed up to the low-hung nest and peeped in. A bright-eyed mother robin was sitting on five small eggs. She looked at the boys and fluttered a little, as if she were frightened.

When they stood motionless, she made no move to fly away.

They were as quiet as mice for about ten minutes. Suddenly they saw the mother robin change her position a little, as if she were making herself more comfortable. It was Aleck's keen ear that heard the small, faint cracking sound of an eggshell breaking. The mother robin lifted her wing and made a little chirruping sound.

Aleck grasped his brother's arm. "Look!" he whispered. "A little bird was just born!"

The boys waited breathlessly. The mother robin moved again. Again Aleck's ear caught that faint, faint crack. Another baby robin had come into the world!

The boys were very excited. They tiptoed out of earshot of the robin family and rushed back to the McGregors' house. They wanted to tell everyone what they had seen.

Mrs. McGregor was pleased to hear about

the new little robins. "I'll go down and look at them after you've gone," she said.

When they got home they scampered up the steep stairs. They opened the front door of their home and went in.

"Mother! Mother!" they cried. They ran to the parlor. Mrs. Bell was sitting by the north window, where the light was best. She was painting a miniature of little Mary Ellen.

"Mother! Mother!" they said again.

Mrs. Bell never raised her smooth brown head from the miniature. She didn't seem to know the boys were in the room. They looked at each other in amazement.

Aleck crossed the room and laid his hand gently on her shoulder. She looked up then.

"How you startled me, Aleck!" she said. "I didn't hear you come in."

Aleck smiled. "I guess you were thinking so hard about the miniature you didn't hear us," he said cheerfully. But he didn't feel cheerful. He knew that his mother was growing deaf. For some time the family had noticed that she was growing hard of hearing.

"Now tell me where you've been and what you've been doing." Mrs. Bell smiled. "I can tell from your faces that you've had an exciting adventure today."

Both boys began to speak at once. Mrs. Bell listened closely. Aleck suddenly realized that she could understand only half of what they were trying to tell her. He motioned to Melville to be quiet. He began again to tell his mother about the robins. He spoke slowly and clearly as he did to Mary Ellen. Then Mrs. Bell understood.

Suddenly he felt happier. It wasn't going to be quite so bad for his mother to become deaf. She belonged to a family who had made it their life-work to help the deaf and dumb. She was luckier than many people.

At the same time he made up his mind to help her as much as he could. He talked to his brothers about it later.

"One of us must always try to be near her," he explained. "She understands what we say. If anyone else is around who talks too fast or too low so she can't hear, we'll be right there and repeat to her what was said."

Even Edward Charles promised to do his part.

"My sons are my second pair of ears," Mrs. Bell would say fondly. "They never let me miss my first."

A Talking Dog

"You are a boy after my own heart," Signor Auguste Benoit Bertini told Aleck. He patted his shoulder. "You love music as I do. When you play the piano you think of nothing else. I wish all my pupils were like that. Did you know you have worked over that one place for an hour? It is late. You must go home."

"It didn't sound right," Aleck answered. "I don't like discords. I think I have it now." He played it over.

"Fine! You have a sensitive ear. You hear more than most people. All musicians are that way, you know."

Aleck got down from the stool and took his music roll under his arm. He said good-by politely and ran out on the street. He felt fine because he had stuck at the music until he had it right. He put his hands in his pockets and began to whistle.

Suddenly he looked around. He had heard feet pattering along behind him. Out of the twilight shadows came a little dog. It was tired and looked as if it had come a long way. Its coat was matted, and it limped.

Aleck dropped to one knee. He held out his hand. The dog came forward and licked his fingers. Aleck knew that it liked him and he liked it. They were friends right away.

"Come home with me, old fellow," he said.

The dog seemed to know what he meant. It followed along obediently.

"Of course you may," Mrs. Bell said when Aleck asked her if he could keep the dog.

She gave the dog a heaping plate of food and made it a soft warm bed behind the kitchen stove. It curled up and went to sleep. It slept all that night and half the next day. When it woke up at last it was a changed dog. It was well again, and rested and happy. It frisked all over the place, wagging its tail.

"I think he's a Skye terrier," Melville said. "What will you call him, Aleck?"

"I guess I'll call him Terry, because he's a terrier," Aleck decided.

So Terry became the family pet. Soon it seemed as if he had always lived with the Bells. They owned a parrot also. Mr. Bell had wanted to see if a parrot could be taught to speak more plainly than usual, if someone with patience taught it. Their parrot knew a great many more words than most birds of its kind, but its voice still sounded unpleasant. Mr. Bell didn't seem to be able to improve that.

Terry and Bennie, the parrot, became great friends. Aleck soon taught the parrot to call the little dog. Terry was always surprised to hear Bennie talk like a man.

"Here, Terry! Terry! Terry!" Bennie would cry and the dog would come running. Then the parrot would laugh. It got to be a regular game for them.

Aleck came out of the kitchen one day with a handful of sunflower seeds. He had a new word to teach Bennie. The parrot was always rewarded by sunflower seeds, which it liked very much.

Terry followed Aleck in to hear the lesson. Bennie learned the new word easily and quickly. Aleck put the sunflower seeds in a white dish in the cage. The parrot immediately took one, cracked it open, and ate the kernel. "This is good," it said, quite like a human being.

Terry sat staring up at the parrot while it

ate the sunflower seeds. Every time it cracked one it said, "This is good!"

All of a sudden Terry went up to Aleck. He opened his mouth and barked, "Woof! Woof!" Then he sat up and begged.

"Why, Terry!" Aleck cried, delighted. "Do you want to learn to talk like Bennie? I think I can make you!"

He ran out to the kitchen and got some meat. Then he took the little dog into his room and closed the door.

"I think you can learn to talk if you try hard enough," he told Terry. "I wonder if there is anything in the mouth of the dog to keep it from talking? Come, let's see!"

Terry sat up on his haunches and began to growl as Aleck had already taught him to do for something to eat. Aleck gave him a taste of the meat. Then, while Terry growled for more, Aleck put his hands on the dog's mouth and throat, pressed gently and tried to make the growling sound like words. Then he took Terry's muzzle in his hands and closed and opened it a number of times. This caused Terry to make a sound like "ma-ma-ma."

Aleck laughed aloud. "He's trying to say 'Mama!'" he thought.

As soon as he took his hands away Terry stopped growling and Aleck gave him a good piece of meat.

So the lesson continued. By the end of it Terry could not only make a sound that seemed to be "ma-ma-ma." He could also say "ga-ga-ga."

Then Aleck had a wonderful idea. His Grandmother Bell was coming for a visit. He would have a surprise for her!

He and Terry worked hard over their lessons. Terry seemed as anxious to learn as Aleck was anxious to teach him. After weeks of patient training the little animal was able to say something that sounded very much like, "How are you, Grandmama?"

The day of Grandmother Bell's visit arrived. The boys were up early. She was a great favorite with all of them. Aleck was the first to spy her carriage turn the corner. He rushed down the stairs to open the door.

She had brought presents for everybody as she always did when she came on a visit.

Later, when she had rested and they were all gathered in the parlor, Grandmother Bell said, "I hear you have a new pet. Where is he? I am very fond of dogs."

"I'll get him," Aleck said. He was excited. Nobody knew about his surprise. Nobody realized how hard he and Terry had been working.

He came back with a plate of meat which he kept behind his back. Terry followed him. Aleck put the plate behind some books on the table, so Grandmother Bell and the others couldn't see it.

Terry could see it plainly, however, and knew it was his reward.

"Come and meet my grandmother, Terry," Aleck told the dog. Terry trotted over to the small, white-haired lady in the armchair. He sat up on his haunches. He began to growl. Aleck began to open and close Terry's mouth and to move his throat muscles with his fingers.

"Ow-ah-oo-ga-ma-ma!" Terry said.

"Why, bless my heart!" Grandmother Bell cried, throwing up her hands in amazement. "He spoke! He said, 'How are you, Grandmama?' Why, that's wonderful, Aleck, wonderful! I never heard a dog speak before! Does your father know about this? Just wait until I tell your grandfather! A dog that speaks!"

Everyone in the family thought a talking dog was a wonderful thing. Everyone admired Aleck's patience in teaching the little dog how to talk. They wanted to know how he did it.

The applause went to Terry's head. He enjoyed himself so much that he wanted to put on another show.

He sat in front of Grandmother Bell whenever he got a chance and howled and howled. But all he did was howl mournfully, because he couldn't speak without Aleck's help.

School Days

"I'D LIKE to go to school with Melville," Aleck said one morning at the breakfast table. "He seems to have a lot of fun with his friends."

Melville stared at his younger brother. He couldn't believe his ears. To think that anyone would ask to go to school! Still, when he stopped to think about it, Melville decided Aleck was right. He didn't mind school too much. In fact, he had fun with his schoolmates.

So the next morning Aleck started off to Mc-Larens's Academy with Melville.

School wasn't a bit what Aleck had expected. He was quite disappointed. He couldn't play all the time as he had imagined Melville did from the stories his brother had told. Of course there were rest periods during the day when the boys rushed out to the playground. But they had to spend long hours studying Latin and Greek and arithmetic and geography. Aleck didn't enjoy these subjects.

"Now if they only had classes in music and how to stuff dead animals!" he told his mother. He had started a collection of the skulls and skeletons of mice and other small animals. He wanted to learn how to mount them properly.

Mrs. Bell laughed. She was trying to make him understand an arithmetic problem, without much success.

"I like to recite and write verses, too," Aleck went on. "Even Mr. McLaren says I'm good at that, Mother."

"I think you'll always excel in the subjects you're interested in, Aleck," Mrs. Bell said.

"Couldn't you try harder to be interested in Latin and Greek and arithmetic?"

"I'll try, Mother," Aleck promised, but he didn't keep his promise. He just didn't seem to be able to make high marks.

Sandy, who went to another school which did not last so late, always waited outside the school building for Aleck. Terry always waited there, too. It was smart of him to find his way through the winding streets of Edinburgh. He never missed a day, no matter what the weather was.

"Let's walk along Princes Street and look in the windows," Aleck said to Sandy one day. It was his favorite walk. He liked Princes Street. It was lined with shops on one side. On the other was a parklike gorge, and then the hill crowned by the old castle where the Kings and Queens of Scotland had once lived.

To two hungry schoolboys the shopwindows were most interesting. The pastry cooks' win-

dows were all filled today with tempting little
mutton pies.

"I've got a ha'penny," Sandy announced. It
was all he had left from the birthday money he
had received the week before.

"Let's buy a pie!" Aleck suggested.

Sandy hesitated. He liked to shop. It gave him
a feeling of being grown up. The two boys went
into the shop and took their time looking over
the things displayed on the counter.

"Shall we buy some Edinburgh Rock sugar candy?" Sandy asked importantly.

He turned the ha'penny over and over in his pocket. In a way he didn't want to spend it. The things in the pastry cook's shop looked so good he knew he would spent it. But he was going to take his time over it.

"Maybe you'd like some shortbread in these pretty tartan wrappings," the old lady behind the counter said.

Sandy shook his head.

"Buy the mutton pie," Aleck whispered. "Then Terry can have some, too."

That settled it. Terry was a great favorite with Sandy. The little Skye terrier wouldn't like candy. So the pie was chosen and Sandy handed over his ha'penny.

The boys divided the small pie evenly. Then they shared their pieces with Terry as they marched along, munching happily.

One thing in school fascinated Aleck. It was an old-fashioned clock that hung on the wall in the main corridor. It had a very loud tick. Melville told Aleck that when he first went to school the clock had a deep, loud chime. It rang out every hour. It was so loud that it bothered the teachers. It took the pupils' minds off their lessons. Mr. McLaren had it fixed so that it didn't chime any more.

"How I'd like to hear that chime," Aleck thought. "How I'd like to see the insides of that old clock!"

One day he found himself alone in the hall. He stared up at the clock. The temptation to see how it worked was too much for him. He pulled a stool over and climbed up. He opened the little door of the compartment where the works were. He put his hand in and felt around. The hammer that struck the bell and made the chimes had been fastened back with a small hook. It took

Aleck only a second to loosen it. It was just three minutes to one in the afternoon. Aleck held his breath while the three minutes passed. Then slowly, but loudly, the old clock whirred and whirred. The deep-voiced, loud chime rang out! One o'clock!

Aleck quickly fastened the hammer back in place and jumped off the stool. Doors opened up and down the corridor. "What was that?" voices asked. "It sounded like the old clock!"

Mr. McLaren came out of the room where he had a Greek class. He disliked Greek as much as Aleck did, but he had to teach it. Teaching something he didn't enjoy made him cross. He saw Aleck push the stool back, and he put two and two together.

"Alexander Graham Bell!" he cried, striding down the hall. "You've been touching the clock! You started it chiming again! Come here!"

Aleck walked toward Mr. McLaren obediently, but slowly. He knew he was going to be punished. He knew he deserved it. He shouldn't have touched the clock. But oh, it was so nice to know how things worked! He wondered if Mr. McLaren had ever felt that way.

"Hold out your hands," Mr. McLaren told him. Aleck obeyed and Mr. McLaren brought down the small birch rod he always carried smack across his palms. It felt like a swarm of bees stinging all at once. Aleck bit his lips.

"There! Let that be a lesson to you! Never touch that clock again!"

Mr. McLaren went back to his room to teach his class some more Greek.

In a few weeks Aleck thought no more about the clock. Once he knew how things looked inside and worked he lost interest in them.

There were many snowstorms that winter. The wind blew sharply across the lonely Scotch moors. Gales from the Atlantic Ocean beat against the shores of Scotland and blew great icy breaths across the land.

Aleck and Sandy hurried along Princes Street now. The weather was too cold for them to stop and stare in the shop windows.

Everybody in Scotland settled down for the long cold winter. Everyone wore warm woolen clothes and piled the stoves full of coal. The temperature stayed below freezing.

The classrooms in McLaren's Academy were warm enough. The teachers kept the black stoves crammed with coal until the sides glowed like rubies. But the long hallways were impossible to heat and they were icy cold.

Aleck was one of the "little fellows." His classes were over an hour earlier than Melville's. Sometimes he waited for his brother so they could walk home together, but it was too cold now to wait in the icy corridor. Even Sandy and Terry didn't call for him when it was cold.

One day Aleck pulled his tam well down around his ears. He buttoned up his coat. He pulled on his mittens. Then he stepped out into the corridor. He closed the door quickly.

My, it was cold! His breath was like a great white cloud. For a moment he pretended he was grown up and smoking a cigar. He puffed on his imaginary cigar and watched his breath float higher and higher, just like smoke.

He walked slowly past the clock. It was ticking in a muffled way as if it felt the cold, too.

He inhaled again on his imaginary cigar. This time it really smelled like a cigar. There was even a taste of smoke in his mouth.

Then he saw smoke, great clouds of smoke, real this time, billowing out from under the door of a room at the end of the corridor. The next minute he heard the crackling of dry wood. The school was on fire!

Aleck wondered what to do. He had to act

quickly. Mr. McLaren and the rest of the teachers had to be warned. The boys should get out of the burning building as quickly as possible.

But he didn't have time to run up and down the long corridor and the stairs.

Then he remembered the clock!

He dragged the stool to it and climbed up. He opened the little door and released the hammer. Then he opened the face of the old clock. Quickly he turned the hands until they both stood at twelve o'clock!

The clock began to whir as it had before. Then, loudly and clearly, it began to chime—one—two—three—four—five——

The door of Mr. McLaren's room burst open just as the clock chimed six.

"Alexander Graham Bell!" Mr. McLaren roared. "I thought I told you never to touch that clock again!"

Aleck didn't answer. He just pointed to the

doorway down the hall. McLaren took one look. He cried, "Make the clock chime again. That will bring them out of their rooms! Keep it up until all the rooms are empty!" Then he ran to get help.

Aleck stood on the stool, turning the hands back to twelve and keeping the clock chiming in its deep loud voice until everyone had come to see what was happening. When they saw, they rushed to help put out the fire.

The excitement was over after a while. The fire was out. Then Mr. McLaren called all the pupils and teachers together into the large assembly hall. He took Aleck's hand and led him up to the platform.

"Here," Mr. McLaren began, "is a brave boy, and not only a brave one but a clever one. He used his head. He knew he wouldn't have time to warn us all by running up and down stairs and knocking on all the doors. He knew time was important if the school was to be saved. So he remembered the clock.

"It is lucky for all of us that Alexander Graham Bell has an inquiring mind. If he hadn't wanted to see how the old clock worked he never would have climbed up and discovered what kept it from chiming. And if he hadn't known how it worked, he would never have been able to warn us of the fire."

Aleck smiled shyly when the boys and teachers cheered him, but he was very happy.

"I'd like to go home now, sir," he said politely.

"He's modest, too." Mr. McLaren laughed.

"Long Live
the Queen!"

MR. MC LAREN greeted his pupils on the door-step. "You are to have a holiday," he told them. "No school today because Her Majesty, Queen Victoria, and the Prince Consort are in Edinburgh. They are at Holyrood Palace."

Aleck and Melville were both excited. Queen Victoria had never seemed like a real person. She was only someone they had heard about and read about. They respected her because she was a kind and just ruler of the British Isles. They had never expected to see her. Not any more than they ever expected to see Santa Claus or the King of Siam or the President of the United States!

Now all they had to do was to walk over to Princes Street and find good places to watch the procession. They would see her riding by in state. Mr. McLaren told his pupils he hoped they would all be there and cheer loyally when their Queen rode by.

"Let's go and get Mary Ellen," Aleck said. "She'll enjoy seeing the Queen, too."

As they hurried toward her house they met Sandy racing along.

"I was afraid I'd miss you," he told Aleck. "I wanted to see the procession with you."

Mary Ellen's mother said she might go with the boys. She was grateful to them for remembering her little deaf daughter.

They found excellent places on Princes Street. By craning their necks they could see quite a distance down the street. They would have a good view of the royal procession.

All the shops were decked in gay bunting.

There were flags flying, too. There were great streamers of the Stuart plaid displayed everywhere. The English Queen was proud of her Scotch blood and she enjoyed her visits to Scotland. Everything and everybody looked festive and happy to greet the Queen and her husband, the Prince.

"Here she comes!" Aleck shouted. He could hear the distant skirling of bagpipes. The weird music set his blood dancing in his veins.

Mary Ellen couldn't hear the music. She watched the pipers march along. Their short tartan kilts were swinging. Their black caps were tilted over their eyes, and the little black ribbons that hung down the back were flying in the wind.

Aleck thought their leader was the handsomest man of them all. He wore a great, high hat of black bearskin. He looked about eight feet tall. He kept his eyes straight ahead. He

didn't seem to know there were cheering crowds
on either side of the street.

Then came a picked guard of Scottish soldiers.
They wore kilts, too, but they wore tam-o'-shan-
ters on their heads. They were just like the ones
the boys were wearing.

"Look!" Aleck suddenly shouted. "There's Jamie Dunlop!" He pointed excitedly.

There at the end of the last line of soldiers was Jamie Dunlop, looking very nice in kilts and tam.

"He marches better than any of them!" Sandy cried. "Hurrah for Jamie Dunlop!"

Jamie's face turned a brick-red, but he never turned his head. He kept his black eyes straight ahead. He stepped out more proudly than ever. His kilt swung from side to side and the barrel of his gun sparkled in the sunlight.

"I didn't know Jamie was a soldier," Sandy said. "Did you?"

"Mother told us he had joined up," Aleck told him. "But she didn't know that he belonged to the regiment that will guard the Queen while she is in Scotland. I must be sure to tell her. She will be glad to know."

At last the Queen's carriage came into view. Since it was a pleasant day the royal couple rode in an open carriage so all their subjects could see them plainly.

"How small the Queen is," Aleck said.

Queen Victoria was very short. She was plump and rather pretty. Her husband was blond and tall and handsome. They looked just as a Queen and a Prince Consort should look. They smiled in a friendly way, yet at the same time they were dignified. The children admired them.

Everyone cheered and cheered and the Queen and the Prince Consort bowed politely. The tall Prince was almost as popular as his little Queen wife. The people loved them both.

Then something happened at the head of the procession. The children couldn't see what it was, but the man in the tall bearskin hat had stopped. The pipers stopped, too. Then the soldiers stopped, and at last the royal carriage.

"What luck!" Melville whispered. "Now we shall have a good long look at Queen Victoria."

The children stared. They wanted to remember every single thing about the royal pair. They never expected to see them as close as this again.

Suddenly the Queen dropped her fan. One minute it was in her hand and she was admiring it. It had been given to her by a group of loyal subjects when she had taken her place in the carriage. Now it was gone.

"Oh, dear! My fan! I've lost it, Albert!" Aleck heard the Queen say to her husband in a low voice.

She had dropped it over the side of the open carriage. Aleck darted out into the street. He stooped and picked up the fan and handed it up to her.

"Thank you!" the Queen said gratefully. She was very glad to see her pretty fan again. "I didn't see it fall," she added.

Aleck had remembered to remove his tam when he handed the fan to the queen. But he was too young to know he shouldn't speak to royalty as he did to ordinary people. He thought the Queen was a nice, kind-faced lady. She was very much like his mother's friends who dropped in of an afternoon for a cup of tea.

"I didn't see it fall either," he said cheerfully. "I heard it."

One of the guards stepped forward, but the Queen waved him away. She was interested in spite of herself.

"You mean you could hear my fan fall?" she asked. "Why, that's amazing! What wonderful hearing you must have!"

She had seen Aleck drop Mary Ellen's hand when he had dashed out to pick up her fan. She smiled and asked, "Has your little sister excellent hearing, too?"

Aleck shook his head.

"That's not my sister. She's a friend, and she's deaf. My father has invented a lot of pictures of the way words look when you speak them. He calls them Visible Speech. He taught them to Mary Ellen, and I helped him. Now she can speak, though she's never heard a sound in her life. My mother is deaf, too, but she can understand everything my brothers and I say to her and we take care of her. Someday I mean to invent a machine that will help deaf people hear. I think sound is the nicest thing in the world."

The Queen stared at him. She was too surprised to speak. Usually people were tongue-tied in front of her. This boy wasn't a bit afraid.

"I can hear a pin drop," Aleck went on. "I really can."

That made Queen Victoria smile. After all, he was only a boy.

"A pin drop!" she repeated. "Did you hear that, Albert? This young lad says he can hear a pin drop."

Aleck flushed when the Prince Consort turned

his head and looked at him. The Prince was plainly surprised at the Queen for talking to a small boy on the street. He looked almost as upset as the guard. Aleck felt the disapproval. He met the Prince's eyes frankly.

"Anybody can hear as well as I can, if they take the time to listen," he said.

The Queen's husband bowed. "Perhaps that is true. I never thought of it," he said graciously.

"I'd rather be able to hear than see things," Aleck went on. He told how he had heard the robin's blue egg crack open.

"I'd like to hear more about the machine you plan to invent——" Queen Victoria began.

By now the procession was under way again. The man with the tall hat had moved on. The pipers and the soldiers, with Jamie Dunlop marching straighter than ever, were following. With his whip the coachman touched the backs of the black horses that pulled the carriage.

Melville reached out and drew Aleck back into the crowd. The royal carriage rolled away.

Before it passed out of sight, however, the Queen turned and looked back over her plump shoulder. She gave Aleck a special, gracious, little farewell wave.

Aleck waved back.

The Talking Machine

"GOOD-BY, GOOD-BY!" the Bell boys cried. They stood on the doorstep and waved until the carriage was out of sight. Mr. Bell was going to London. He was going to hear Professor Faber's "speaking machine." The boys would have liked to go, too. A speaking machine would be even more interesting than a talking dog. The boys could hardly wait to hear about the new invention from their father.

At last Mr. Bell returned home. The boys scarcely waited for him to take off his hat and coat before they began to ask questions. Mr. Bell always visited Grandfather and Grandmother

Bell in London. He met many interesting people there. The boys wanted to hear all about them as well as the talking machine.

"First I must have my supper," Mr. Bell said with a laugh.

When supper was over Aleck said, "Now tell about the speaking machine." He had saved the best thing for the last. "Did it really talk? And what made it do so?"

"I was disappointed," Mr. Bell said. "It made noises, but so does a leaky bellows. Perhaps I expected too much."

"Just the same I'd like to see it," Aleck sighed. "Maybe, if I did, I could make one."

"Why don't you try to invent one for yourself?" his father asked. "You and Melville could make it. If you can make one as good as Professor Faber's, I'll give you each a prize."

"Let's try!" Aleck cried excitedly. "Will you help me, Melville?"

"Yes, I will," Melville said. He thought it would be fun.

"How shall we start?" Aleck asked his father.

"Think about yourselves. Think about the things that help you to talk. Your lungs, your throat, your tongue, and your lips," Mr. Bell said.

"I'll make the head," Aleck exclaimed. "I wish I were as good as Melville. He can make anything. But I'll work it out some way."

Mr. Bell smiled. He was pleased that Aleck was going to "work it out." Aleck was clumsy with his hands. He didn't use tools well.

Aleck thought and thought. Finally he said, "I know what I'll do! I'll make the head of gutta-percha. It's easy to handle. It gets soft when you put it in water. If I keep my hands wet, it won't stick. I can mold it in any shape I want. When it cools it will be hard and firm. Then I can give it a fine finish by smoothing it all over with a warm knife."

"That's an excellent idea," Mr. Bell told him. "A pencil of gutta-percha can be handled like a stick of sealing wax. It will melt if you hold it over a candle."

Aleck nodded. "I know. The melted drops stick to any hard surface. They stick better than glue. When I want to fasten pieces of wood together, I always rub them with gutta-percha and just press them together. They stick so well I don't have to use tacks or nails or screws."

"I see you have worked out a way to make the head. Now go on from there," Mr. Bell said.

He took a great interest in the talking machine. He encouraged his sons in every way. He thought it was a valuable educational toy. As they worked on it, they learned what made people speak. They learned what positions the tongue and lips take to form certain words.

"What will you make the lungs of?" Aleck asked Melville.

108

Melville showed him a pair of old bellows. "I'll use these," he said. "I'll make the vocal cords of rubber."

"I'll make the tongue out of rubber and stuff it full of cotton wool," Aleck decided, after feeling his own tongue. The machine tongue should be soft and pliable, too.

The brothers worked hard and well. They soon had a machine which they thought said "Mama" quite plainly.

Melville put it all together. "We'll invite Mother and Father to hear it this evening," he said when it was finished.

"I'd like to ask the Cunninghams, too," Aleck said. "I want to see Sandy's face when he hears it. He's been teasing me. He said we'd never be able to make anything that would really talk. I want to show him."

So he went across the hall and invited the Cunningham family. They all were glad to come.

When everyone was comfortably seated, the boys brought in the odd-looking machine. Aleck hadn't bothered to make eyes or a nose for his head. But he had made a very big mouth with red lips. Through them could be seen the red rubber tongue stuffed with cotton. The vocal cords were all inside a box that formed the neck of the machine. This rested on another box which held the pair of bellows that were the creature's lungs.

Terry ran up and barked at it. He didn't like it a bit. Even the parrot eyed it suspiciously.

Melville set to work on the bellows. He pumped them hard. Aleck pulled the different strings and levers that made the rubber tongue and lips move.

"Mama! Mama!" said the talking machine.

"Gracious me!" Mrs. Cunningham cried. "I've never heard anything like it!"

Even Mrs. Bell was able to hear it.

Mr. Bell was very pleased. "You shall each have a prize. It sounds every bit as good as Professor Faber's. We'll go shopping tomorrow and you shall choose what you want."

Melville knew what he wanted: a new set of tools. Aleck couldn't make up his mind so quickly. There were so many things he wanted. It was hard to make a choice. He would spend a pleasant half hour before he went to sleep, thinking things over.

Aleck hadn't been in bed long before Melville came in. He was older and he could stay up later. "Are you asleep, Aleck?" he whispered.

"No," Aleck answered. He sat up in bed. "What is it?"

Melville lighted the bedside candle.

"Get up and put some clothes on," he whispered. "I've got an idea! Let's take our talking machine downstairs to the front hall and make it cry! The neighbors won't know what it is!"

111

Aleck hopped out of bed. He thought it was a wonderful idea. He loved a bit of mischief.

He dressed and then the boys opened the bedroom door quietly. They listened. They heard no sound. The rest of the flat was dark. Their parents had gone to bed and Edward Charles was fast asleep.

They carried the machine between them. It was rather heavy. They tiptoed down through the dark building. There was only a tiny pin point of light on every landing, but that was enough for the two mischievous boys.

They reached the lower hall without anyone's hearing them. They set up the machine under the stairs. Melville began to blow the bellows and Aleck began to pull the strings.

"Mama! Mama! Mama!" the machine wailed. It sounded even more human than it had the first time. The narrow halls and stairs carried its voice better. "Mama! Mama! Mama!"

Doors opened all over the house. Voices asked "What's that? Do you hear what I hear?"

"It sounds like a little child," a kind woman said. "I'll go down and see. Perhaps a baby has been left on the doorstep!"

The Bell boys heard her coming down the stairs. They put their hands over their mouths to cover their laughter. They thought it was an excellent joke. The woman went to the front door and opened it.

"You poor wee darling——"she began.

But there wasn't any baby there! She stepped out into the street and looked up and down. The street was empty!

"Well, I declare!" she said. "I'm sure I heard a baby cry for its mother."

She came in and climbed the stairs again.

"Not a sign of a baby anywhere," she told her interested neighbors. She shut her door. Other doors closed, too.

114

The boys waited until all was quiet. Then the talking machine cried again.

"Mama! Mama! Mama!" it wailed.

Again doors flew open. Again the kindhearted woman stepped out.

"There it is again, poor thing," she said. "I wonder if it could have been in the hall? Under the stairs, perhaps?" She started down the stairs again. "I'll go down and see."

The boys looked around for some place to hide their machine. They didn't want to be found out yet!

To get to the back door, however, they would have to pass in front of the stairs. They could be seen by all the people peering over the banisters above.

"I guess we'd better confess," Aleck said.

He sighed. It had been a lot of fun, but he was sure his father would be angry. He would punish them. They probably wouldn't get their wonderful prizes. Aleck was suddenly glad he hadn't decided on his. He wouldn't be so disappointed as Melville.

The woman had reached the lower hall. In a moment she would find them.

Then the boys heard their father's voice. "I think I know what that is," Mr. Bell said. "I must apologize. My boys invented a machine which can say 'Mama' quite distinctly. They must be playing a trick with it. They must be down in the hall. I'll go and get them. I hope you'll forgive them for disturbing you. I'm afraid they have the enthusiasm of all inventors."

"Do you mean to say your boys invented a machine that can talk as well as that?" asked Mrs. McLane, who had searched for the baby.

"Yes," Mr. Bell answered. He couldn't keep pride out of his voice, even though he was annoyed with the boys.

"Well, I think it's wonderful!" she cried.

"Don't you punish them, Mr. Bell. It might discourage them so they'd never invent another thing all the rest of their lives! Boys as smart as that should be praised. No telling what they may invent someday."

"That's very kind of you, Mrs. McLane," Mr. Bell said gratefully.

Aleck and Melville had picked up their machine. Now they came out from the shadows under the stairs.

"Thank you, Mrs. McLane, for not being angry," Aleck said politely. "We didn't mean any harm. We just wanted to see if our machine really sounded like a baby."

"It certainly did!" Mrs. McLane cried. "Let me see the contraption. Show us how it works."

Aleck and Melville set up their machine. All the people came and sat on the stairs. When the machine said, "Mama! Mama!" in its lifelike way everyone clapped his hands.

Another Birthday

"I DON'T know whether I'm going to like the country," Aleck told Sandy.

They were taking a last walk together down Princes Street. The Bells were moving to a cottage outside Edinburgh. "I won't see as much of you as before."

"Oh, I'll come and visit you often," Sandy said. He wanted to cheer Aleck up. He didn't feel very happy himself. They had been best friends for a great many years.

They walked along and looked in shopwindows. Aleck like to pretend he was grown-up and rich. He picked out the presents he would buy then for everyone he liked. He would buy a beautiful gold chain with a heart locket for his mother. He would buy his father a heavy watch chain. A gold-headed cane would be just right for his grandfather.

His grandmother would like a needlecase made in the shape of Edinburgh Castle. Melville should have a set of tools, even better than those Mr. Bell had given him. Little Edward Charles would be pleased with a horse and wagon Aleck himself liked. Signor Bertini should have——

Sandy pulled at his sleeve. "What are you dreaming about?" he asked.

"I was choosing presents that I shall buy for my family when I am old and rich," Aleck explained. "See that horse and wagon? I'll get that for Edward Charles."

"When you're old and rich, he'll be old too," Sandy pointed out. "What will he want with a horse and wagon then?"

Aleck stared at Sandy. How smart he was! Aleck hadn't thought of that.

They stopped at their favorite pastry cook's shop for two mutton pies. How good they tasted!

"I suppose it will be a long time before I have another," Aleck sighed. "I don't think there are pastry cooks in the country."

"You'd think you were going to China!" Sandy laughed. "Why, you're coming back to Edinburgh once a week for your music lesson. Have you forgotten? I'll see you then."

"That's right," Aleck cried. "Now I feel better!" He raced Sandy all the way home.

If Sandy had lived near by, Aleck would have liked the country very much. He liked Milton Cottage. It was fun to live in a house instead of a flat. It didn't matter how much noise he made, or how often he clattered up and down the stairs. Nobody ever complained.

There were many new things to do. The boys

120

all collected minerals, wild flowers, beetles, and birds' eggs. Aleck dissected many field mice. He added their skulls to his collection. In an old summerhouse he set up a museum to display his collection of the skeletons of small animals.

He decided that he liked the country, but he still missed Sandy.

Once a week Aleck went in the mail cart to Edinburgh for his music lesson. Sandy was always at the corner where the cart stopped to let Aleck down. Although the boys saw each other only once a week, they were still best friends. Aleck was sure that there was no friend like Sandy in the world. Sandy knew there was no one like Aleck.

Sandy always went to Signor Bertini's house with Aleck and waited while Aleck had his lesson. Sandy liked music well enough, but not enough to take lessons. "Whenever I want to hear some I can visit you," he told Aleck.

One day in early March Sandy stood on the corner blowing on his hands and stamping his feet. The day was cold and the mail cart late.

At last it turned the corner and Aleck hopped out. He didn't look cold. He seemed to feel fine. That made Sandy cross. His hands were so cold he wanted Aleck's to be cold, too. Aleck didn't notice his crossness. He had news.

"Day after tomorrow is my birthday and we're having a party," he told Sandy. "Mother said I was to invite you and your family. Please come, Sandy."

A party! Sandy forgot his crossness. He knew the Bells always gave nice parties.

When Aleck's lesson was over he and Signor Bertini came out of the music room.

"Please remember the party starts at eight o'clock," Aleck said. He had invited his teacher to the birthday party, too.

"I'll not forget," Signor Bertini assured him.

122

"I would not miss seeing your grandfather's pleasure when he hears this new piece you have learned for him. You have done well, Aleck. You play it perfectly."

"Thank you, sir," Aleck said politely.

Signor Bertini patted his shoulder. "Someday you will give a concert," he said. "I shall sit in a box with Sandy, and we shall applaud very hard. Eh, Sandy? I shall be very proud of my former pupil. You wait and see!"

Aleck smiled. It was a pleasant picture, but Aleck wasn't sure he wanted to be a musician. Ever since he and Melville had made the talking machine he had been interested in inventing things. He wasn't sure just what he wanted to do when he grew up.

"I have two presents for my grandfather," he told Sandy. "I want to buy him another. Let's go to Princes Street."

He found what he wanted in the very first

shop. It was a plaid necktie. Aleck had saved just enough pocket money for it.

"Now I have the tie, a new piano piece, and a poem I've written," he told Sandy. "I'll recite it for you," he offered.

Sandy said, "All right." He didn't like poetry much, but he didn't mind Aleck's. He thought Aleck was clever to make it up.

"I am thirteen years old, I find,
    Your birthday and mine are the same.
I wish to inherit your mind,
    As well as your much-honored name.
Today you are threescore and ten:
    Your once raven locks are now white,
You have reached the allotment of men.
    With a heart that's both cheerful and light.
Live on still in comfort and peace,
    Your cares loving friends will allay,
May you have of this life a long lease;
    Many happy returns of the day!"

"That's fine!" Sandy said. "He'll like that very much, Aleck."

124

The mail cart came around the corner. The driver called, "Hurry up! There'll be snow before we get home."

Aleck scrambled into the cart. "Don't forget the party!" he called.

The day of the party arrived at last. Aleck recited his poem over and over again to himself. He was afraid he might forget it. He hoped his grandfather would like it. Then he thought, "Perhaps he'd like a copy of it. That would make another present. Then he could read it to himself after he goes home."

He asked his mother if he might borrow a sheet of her note paper.

"Yes, of course, Aleck," she said. "It's in my small lap desk."

It took Aleck some time to choose the piece he wanted. Some of the paper had little flowers in the corners. That didn't look mannish. "Flowers are for girls," he thought.

He chose a piece of plain, heavy white paper and carried it back to his room.

He sat down at his desk and took out a new pen. He dipped it in the ink and began to write. He was anxious to get every word spelled right. He wanted the poem to look nice. The tip of his tongue stuck out of the corner of his mouth as he bent over the table.

He finished it at last and sat back to admire it.

"Many happy returns of the day to Grandpapa Bell," he had headed the poem. It looked very nice, he thought.

But it needed something else to finish it off. He drew a small picture of a bell. That would stand for both his and his grandfather's name. Bell! His grandfather would be pleased.

Aleck like the picture of the bell so much that he said to himself, "I think I'll use that picture as a sort of trade-mark. I'll sign everything I do with a picture of a bell. It will be different." Aleck always liked anything that was different.

He folded the paper neatly and sealed it with a gob of red wax. He carried it into the parlor and put it on the table that held the other gifts for his grandfather. On the table that held his gifts there were four packages already. The family hadn't forgotten him!

He could scarcely wait for the party to begin. He couldn't eat much supper. At last it was time for him to get dressed. The guests would start to arrive soon.

Aleck's grandparents were coming from London. If their train wasn't held up by the fog, they should arrive before the other guests and have time for a rest before the party. After all, as Grandmother Bell often said, they weren't so spry as they used to be.

The McGregors were now such old friends that they seemed like part of the family. Mr.

McGregor and Mrs. McGregor came in, and Aleck greeted them happily.

"You look exactly the way you did when I first met you," Aleck said to Mr. McGregor. "That was six years ago."

The old Scotch shepherd laughed. It made his weather-beaten face crinkle up. It showed his toothless gums.

"I guess I've looked almost the same since I was a boy," he said. "When you're out with the sheep in all kinds of weather, winter and summer, laddie, it ages you. Then nobody can tell your real age. Shepherding is good for the soul, but it's hard on the body." He laughed again.

Somebody played a gay rat-a-tat-tat on the front door with the polished brass knocker.

"That's Grandfather!" Aleck rushed away to greet him.

"The fog held us up again," Grandmother Bell explained. "It's always bad at this time of year."

Other guests came. The piles of presents on the tables by the door grew and grew. Mrs. Bell lighted the candles on the birthday cakes. Then it was time to open the presents.

When all the paper had been collected and burned in the fireplace and the string and ribbons wound into neat balls, Mr. Bell made an announcement. "Aleck has two more presents for his grandfather."

Aleck seated himself at the piano. Signor Bertini, looking very pleased, found a good seat. Mrs. Bell sat down close to the piano. She wanted to hear as much as possible. Sometimes, when she and Aleck were alone and he was practicing she would lay her ear right against the piano. Then she could hear very well, she declared. She could hear the vibrations of the keys through the polished rosewood.

Aleck played his new piece. Everyone applauded. They wanted to hear more. So he played several other pieces. People liked to hear Aleck play. His music made then remember pleasant, happy things.

Now it was time for the poem. Aleck stood by the fireplace. His cheeks were red with excitement. He was just a little nervous. His grandfather taught people to speak carefully and clearly. He wouldn't stand for any slurring of words. Especially from his grandson!

Aleck spoke slowly and distinctly. He rounded out each word as he had been taught by his grandfather and his father. The human voice was a beautiful thing when it was properly used, both men said. It was just laziness that made people slur their words.

"That was fine!" Grandfather Bell cried. "You recite very well."

Aleck handed his grandfather the paper with the dashing red seal. The old man put on his spectacles. Then he broke the seal.

"You couldn't have given me a present I liked better," Grandfather Bell said, when he had read the poem. "It was nice to hear you recite it so well. I am glad to have this carefully written copy. Now I can read it whenever I like. Who gave you the idea of signing it with a bell? That was very clever."

"I thought of that myself," Aleck answered. He flushed proudly. "The bell is going to be my trade-mark when I grow up."

Signor Auguste Benoit Bertini threw up his hands when he heard this. "What do you mean, lad?" he cried in surprise. "One does not have a trade-mark when one is a musician!"

"Maybe Aleck isn't going to be a musician," Grandfather Bell said quickly. He looked at Signor Bertini from under his heavy black eyebrows. "There are other things to do than play the piano, you know. Maybe Aleck will decide to help the deaf to hear and the dumb to speak

132

just as his father and I have done. There is nothing wrong about that!"

At that moment Aleck knew that was exactly what he wanted to do!

"And not only that," he added, thinking of the talking machine, "I want to invent things in my spare time."

A Visit to London

MRS. BELL held an opened letter in her hand. She looked excited and happy.

"It's from your grandfather," she said to Aleck. "He wants you to visit him in London. How would you like that?"

Aleck shook his head. "I don't know," he answered honestly. "I'd like to see London, but I'd miss you and the rest of the family. I'd miss Sandy, too, and I don't think Grandfather would know any boys in London."

"Think it over," Mrs. Bell advised. "It's fun to travel and see new places."

So Aleck decided to go.

Once he had made up his mind, it was fun to get ready for the long journey. A train trip would be an adventure. He began to feel grown-up and important. He was glad he had decided to go.

All of the family and Sandy Cunningham went to see him off.

Aleck climbed aboard and found a seat by the window so he could look out on the passing countryside. He had made up his mind to leave his family with a cheerful smile. It was hard at the last minute. He knew they loved him and wished him well. He didn't want to leave them, now that the time had come. However, he remembered what he had promised himself, and he kept on smiling bravely through the window.

He waved until the train was out of sight. Then he took out his handkerchief and blew his nose and swallowed a big lump in his throat.

"Here, take this," a kind voice said.

A lady in a big black hat with a blue plume

held out a peppermint candy to him. "It will make you feel better," she said with a smile.

"Thank you," he said politely.

The cold mint taste was pleasant. He sat quietly looking out the window. He rolled the candy under his tongue. After a while he did feel better. He began to take an interest in things.

"The more I see and remember, the more I can write and tell the family," he thought.

At last he arrived in London. The station seemed immense. How would he ever find his grandfather in this crowd? Suppose he didn't find him? What could he do? Then he put his hand on his wallet and felt better. There was enough money in it to buy a ticket back to Edinburgh. Wouldn't his family be surprised to see him back so soon! He almost wished that he couldn't find his grandfather.

Then he saw a tall gray beaver hat coming toward him. Grandfather Bell would be under it.

He still wore the kind of hat that was popular when he was young. There probably wasn't another like it in London.

"I'm very glad to see you, Aleck," he said.

Looking up into the kind old face, Aleck knew that he was glad he had decided to come. He was very fond of his grandfather.

Aleck thought London was a very smoky city. Smoke hung in black clouds low above the roofs. But the city had the magic of a new place for Aleck. He sniffed at the air, expecting it to smell differently—and it did!

"I wish we had time for a little drive," Grandfather Bell said, as they drove to his house. "There are a great many places in London I want to show you. But I have a class to teach this evening. Would you like to come?"

"I'd like it very much. I'm going to like doing everything in this big city. Everything is going to be different and interesting," Aleck answered.

138

"It will be, at first." Grandfather Bell smiled. "You'll soon grow used to it."

Grandfather's house at Number 18 Harrington Square face the tall iron railings of Harrington Gardens across the street.

"The gardens are named for a kind old earl," Grandfather Bell told Aleck. "He used to wear a sage-green hat when he walked among his trees so that he would not frighten the birds that nested in them."

Aleck laughed. He wished the old earl was alive now so he could talk to him. He would have liked to tell him how he had heard the robin's eggs crack open.

"Only we people who live around the square have keys to the park," Grandfather Bell went on. "It is a very nice place for a stroll. I hope you will go there often."

A white-capped maid opened the door for them. She led Aleck to a large front room overlooking the park. It was a friendly room, with gay chintz curtains and a four-posted bed with curtains to match. Best of all, there was a fireplace in it with a cheerful coal fire. Aleck knew he would be happy in this room.

The big drawers of the tall highboy swallowed his few belongings. His Sunday suit, which was the only other one he had, looked lonely in the big old wardrobe.

He washed his hands and face and combed his hair. The train trip had made him feel gritty and dirty. Then he went to join his grandfather downstairs in the drawing room.

Grandmother Bell had died. Grandfather Bell was lonely, so he had asked Aleck to come and stay with him. The big house was too quiet when there was no one to share it with him.

Aleck knocked on the door of the drawing room. His grandfather was sitting before the fire. He was a handsome old gentleman. His white hair was as thick and crisp as his grand-son's and it mussed as easily. He and Aleck both had what his grandfather called "the big Bell nose." His eyes, too, were dark like Aleck's.

Aleck walked across the room. His grand-father's keen black eyes looked him over from head to foot.

"You'll need some new clothes," Mr. Bell said sharply. "Rough tweeds are all very well for Scotland. While you're in London you must dress as the boys do here."

Aleck thought that some new clothes would be nice. He had always wanted a blue suit with silver buttons.

"I'll take you to my tailor tomorrow," Grand-father Bell promised.

After supper Mr. Bell's class began to arrive. There were about half a dozen young ladies and half a dozen young men. Nobody had to sit be-hind a desk or write on slates. They just sat anywhere they liked in the drawing room. It was really more like a party than a class.

Aleck sat quietly in a corner after his grandfather had introduced him.

Grandfather Bell sat by the fire. He held a copy of William Shakespeare's plays in his hand. He didn't really need it for he knew almost all the plays by heart. Tonight the class was reading aloud the one called *Hamlet*.

The young ladies and gentlemen took turns reading aloud. Grandfather Bell corrected them gently when they made mistakes.

The next morning Grandfather Bell took Aleck to his tailor. Mr. Bullick was a small, fussy man. His tailoring shop was one of the best in London. Grandfather Bell had been his customer for years.

"I want you to fit my grandson out properly," Mr. Bell said. "We would like to have the new clothes as soon as possible."

142

"Beautiful material," Mr. Bullick said. He pinched a piece of Aleck's tweed jacket between his fingers. "But not right for London. Oh, no, not right for London."

"I'd like a dark blue suit with silver buttons," Aleck said.

Mr. Bullick looked at Mr. Bell. They both shook their heads. "Not dark blue," Mr. Bullick said. "Oh, no, indeed."

"We'll leave it to you," Mr. Bell said firmly. "You know what the boys in London are wearing nowadays, Bullick."

"Indeed I do," Mr. Bullick agreed. "They are not wearing blue suits with silver buttons. Oh, no, indeed!"

After Mr. Bullick measured him, Aleck could hardly wait for his new clothes to arrive.

"Wait until Sandy hears I have a new suit just like London boys' clothes," he thought, and chuckled. "And Melville and Edward Charles!"

The new clothes came at last. Aleck rushed downstairs and took the boxes. He carried them to his room. His hands shook with excitement. His fingers seemed to turn to thumbs. He had a hard time with the knots, but he got the lids off at last.

He took out the clothes. He looked at them in amazement. He had never seen anything like them before!

He took off his good, heavy tweed suit and hung it carefully away in the closet. Then he put on the new clothes and looked at himself in the long mirror.

He didn't know whether to laugh or cry.

"I look like a dressed-up monkey!" he said to himself. "Just like a monkey!"

He stared at himself. The black and gray striped trousers were uncomfortably tight. The Eton jacket stopped short at his waist. The wide white collar of the shirt nipped at his chin. The only thing that seemed familiar was the loose black bow tie. He had worn one like that with his own suit. Another box revealed a tall silk hat. And in a long narrow box was a cane.

"If Sandy ever saw me dressed up like this, I'd never hear the end of it. I'd never be able to live it down," he thought.

Then he thought on: "Grandfather can't make me dress this way! I look more and more like a monkey the more I put on. Maybe Mr. Bullick made a mistake. Maybe this was made for a fancydress party. Maybe these silly clothes belong to somebody else."

His grandfather called from downstairs. Aleck went slowly down. He hoped he wouldn't meet the maid. He didn't want anyone to see him, not even his grandfather. But when Grandfather Bell called, Aleck knew he had to obey. There was not time to get back into his tweed suit.

"Let me look at you," Grandfather Bell cried

when Aleck stepped into the drawing room. Aleck's cheeks were as red as the carpet. He had even forgotten to put down the silly cane. He was still clutching it in his hand.

"Mr. Bullick has done an excellent job," Grandfather Bell said approvingly. "You wouldn't know yourself, would you, Aleck?"

"I certainly wouldn't!" Aleck said unhappily. "If my brothers or any of my friends saw me, they'd laugh and tease me for the rest of my life."

"Nonsense!" Grandfather Bell said. "I only wish your mother were here to see you. You look very handsome indeed. Not a bit like the rough little Scotch lad I met at the station. Yes, Mr. Bullick has done a very good job. I must compliment him the next time I see him."

"Do I have to wear these clothes?" Aleck asked forlornly. "I thought Mr. Bullick had made a mistake and sent the wrong ones."

"Of course you must wear them," Grandfather

Bell declared. "They are what boys wear here. He sent you two suits, I hope. One for every day and one for Sundays."

"Yes, sir." Aleck nodded.

He turned and rushed blindly from the room. The new clothes had suddenly made him homesick. They made him see how different everything in London was from Edinburgh.

He would have given anything to have seen his family at that minute, or to have spoken to them. But he realized suddenly how many miles and miles of land separated him from those whom he loved.

He wished again that there was some way a person could speak to someone he loved, even though he was in a different country.

A Gypsy's Prophecy

GRANDFATHER BELL looked up from his book.
Aleck stood in the doorway, first on one foot,
then on the other. Grandfather Bell had sent
for him because he was displeased about something. Aleck was trying to remember what he
had done wrong.

"Yes, Grandfather?" he said politely.

"Come here, Aleck," Mr. Bell said sternly,
putting down his book.

Aleck had seldom heard his grandfather use
such a serious tone of voice. He must be very
much displeased.

However, it wasn't anything he had done but

148

so something he had neglected to do that worried his grandfather.

"I'm surprised to find, Aleck, that you know no Latin to speak of, and no Greek."

Aleck dropped his eyes and twiddled his thumbs slowly. He remembered the years at Mr. McLaren's Academy. How discouraged his teachers had been when it came to getting Latin and Greek into his stubborn black head!

"I never liked to study such things," he tried to explain. "I like writing verses and reciting and inventing things——"

"I must admit you do all those things very well," Grandfather Bell said. He remembered the poem Aleck had written and recited for him. He remembered the talking machine. "But every gentleman knows Latin and Greek. You must study both while you are with me. I shall take you in hand and outline your studies."

Aleck felt sorry that he had neglected his first

chances to study. He made up his mind to change. He would study hard and become a person Grandfather Bell would be proud of.

"Am I going to school?" he asked.

Mr. Bell shook his head. "No, you will study at home with me."

Aleck went back to his own room. He was glad he didn't have to go to school. He still felt uncomfortable in his new clothes. He knew how his brothers and Sandy would laugh if they saw him in the tight suit. English schoolboys would probably do the same.

He looked at himself in the mirror. He looked rather white and sickly. That was because he wasn't getting enough fresh air, he decided. He must get out more.

Still, he couldn't go out in the new clothes. He went to the big wardrobe where his Sunday suit had looked so lost. He opened the heavy mahogany doors and looked inside. His tweeds were gone! Only another suit, as tight and un-comfortable as the first, hung there.

Aleck rang the bell and waited for the maid to come to his room.

"Have you seen my suits? The ones I brought from Scotland?" he asked.

She shook her head. "No, sir," she said. "I'd ask Mr. Bell if I were you."

Aleck ran downstairs to ask his grandfather.

"Why, yes, I have seen your suits," Grand-father Bell said quietly. "I gave them to Joseph, our handy man. He has a son just your age and build. I dislike to see anything go to waste. I knew you would have no need for those clothes here in London. When you go back to Scotland you will have outgrown them."

Anger choked Aleck for a minute, but he bit back his reply. He went up to his room again. When he thought it over he knew that his grand-father was right. He wouldn't need the tweed suits in London. On the few walks he had taken on the London streets he had seen that English people didn't wear heavy tweeds or clump around in thick-soled boots. But he hadn't yet seen any other boys dressed in clothes like his.

He looked down at the tops of the trees in the little park. The window was open and the soft breeze came in pleasantly. It would be good to get out in it and take a brisk walk, but he didn't want to face the street alone.

He remembered what his grandfather had told him the day of his arrival. People who lived around the square had keys to the gate of the little park. He would get the key and take his walk there under the trees. He wouldn't be likely to meet any boys his own age now.

Tessie, the maid, showed him where the big iron key hung behind the basement door.

"Be sure to take your cane with you," she told him. "Little gentlemen always carry their canes."

He ran to get the hateful cane. He tucked it under his arm. He felt silly in the high silk hat and the tight trousers and the short Eton jacket. How could English boys play cricket in such uncomfortable clothes. How could they have any fun at all?

He hurried across the street and let himself into the park. It appeared quite empty. He walked down a shadowed path and drew in deep breaths of the sweet air. It was good to be out!

It was good to feel the sunshine. It would be nice here if Sandy were only with him!

He pushed the tall silk hat to the back of his head and thrust his hands into the pockets of the striped gray trousers. He felt better. He would have hidden the cane behind a bush, but he was afraid Grandfather Bell would be angry.

He began to whistle. He wished that in some mysterious way he could get in touch with his family and friends in Scotland. He didn't exactly want to see them. They might howl with laughter. But he would like to tell them about London. He would like to tell them about this park in the midst of the busy city. It was like a small bit of country shut in behind iron railings and a gate.

If there were only some way you could talk to people far away!

Then, coming down the path toward him, he saw a boy. A boy dressed exactly as he was! It

154

seemed too good to be true. The boy even carried a cane and he was whistling, too!

They met in the middle of the path. They stopped and stared at each other in surprise. Then they began to laugh! It was a good beginning for a new friendship.

"My name is Alexander Graham Bell," Aleck said in his friendly way.

"I'm James Murray," the boy answered.

From that day onward Aleck's life in London changed. He spent the morning studying with his grandfather. He made fine progress. Grandfather Bell was pleased with him. After a heavy midday dinner, Grandfather Bell took a nap. Aleck slipped out and went for long walks with his new friend, James Murray.

He didn't mind walking now that he had a friend dressed exactly like him. He soon discovered that other boys dressed the same way, too. The new clothes became familiar. He felt at home in them. Even the cane didn't bother him much.

While they walked the boys talked about everything under the sun.

"I'm going to write a dictionary," James Murray announced. "I'm already collecting words for it. It will have more words and their meanings than any dictionary in the world."

"I think a dictionary ought to help you pronounce words, too," Aleck said. "My father invented a lot of little marks which he put over the words in our readers when he taught us to read. They made it easier for us to learn how to say new words."

"That's a very good idea," James Murray said. "I'd like to meet your father."

"You must come to Scotland and stay with us," Aleck answered. "You'll like all my family and they will like you."

James promised he would someday.

"You'd like Edinburgh Castle and Holyrood Castle, too," Aleck said. He told James about seeing the Queen and the Prince Consort.

"Let's go to Madam Tussaud's waxworks exhibit," James cried eagerly. "They have a wax figure of Queen Victoria there. You can tell me if it really look like her."

So the boys went to the famous Madam Tussaud's. Here were wax figures of all the famous people in the world. There were Napoleon; Mary, Queen of Scots; the English Queen Elizabeth; and even William Shakespeare, whose plays Grandfather Bell admired so much.

On another afternoon walk, they saw a large sign on Egyptian Hall. It said: "SEE GENERAL TOM THUMB, THE SMALLEST MAN IN THE WORLD."

The boys paid their shillings. They pushed their way into the crowded hall. At the end of the room on a high platform, so all might see him,

157

stood the midget. A big sign was hung on the wall behind him:

"General Tom Thumb, the Smallest Man in miniature in the known world, weighing only fifteen pounds and standing only two feet, one inch, in his shoes."

The little general was indeed a sight to see. He was dressed exactly like Aleck and Jim Murray. That made them laugh heartily. His small cane was only a foot long. His silk hat was a few inches high.

At last they turned away from the little man. They had listened to him sing several songs in his high treble voice and watched him do a little dance on the platform.

As they went out, they bumped into a tall man in a silk hat. He was smoking a big cigar, almost as long as Tom Thumb's cane.

"Hello there!" he said in a deep bass voice. "Have you seen the general?"

"Yes, sir," Aleck answered.

"You like to see odd thing, don't you? Boys always do. So do grown folks. I aim to please them all. I collect odd things. Then I show them to people. My name is Phineas T. Barnum. Ever hear of me?"

"No, sir," Aleck said honestly.

"Well, if you lived in America you would have heard of me." The big man laughed. "I own a museum in New York City. I've got a real live mermaid on exhibit there. If you ever cross the ocean to America, come to see me. I'll show you a thing or two."

He handed each boy a large white card with his name printed on it. Suddenly he added, "Why don't you have Madam Rockwell tell your fortunes. She's the best fortuneteller in the world. Only costs you two bits."

"Two bits?" Aleck repeated. "Two bits of what, sir?"

Mr. Barnum threw back his head and laughed. "Forgot for a second I was in England!" he shouted. "Two bits is what we call a quarter in America. Costs you two shillings here."

"We can't do it then," Aleck said politely. "I've spent half of my week's allowance already."

Besides he wasn't at all sure his family would approve. They didn't believe in fortunetellers.

"Come along! Come along!" Mr. Barnum said heartily. "It will be my treat. I'll tell Madam Rockwell you're my friends. She'll give you a good fortune."

"Let's!" James Murray whispered. "I'd like to know if I'm going to write that dictionary when I grow up."

Aleck decided Grandfather Bell wouldn't mind too much, if he didn't believe everything the fortuneteller told him.

So he followed Mr. Barnum and James to another room in Egyptian Hall. A big sign told of the wonderful power of Madam Rockwell to see the past, present and future.

Mr. Barnum made the most of that short walk to the fortuneteller's room. He told the boys how wonderful Madam Rockwell was. She could read the future in the stars or cards or even in the palm of one's hand. While he talked, he looked around to see that other people heard what he was saying. A great many people stopped to listen to his booming voice. When the boys slipped through the curtains into Madam Rockwell's room, there was a good-sized crowd outside, waiting to have their fortunes told.

The fortuneteller was a kind-looking woman dressed in dirty, gypsylike clothes. She made the boys sit on stools across the table from her. Then she took their hands and stared into their palms. She had long black hair. Her hands, though dirty, were covered with rings.

"There's fame and fortune ahead of you both,"

162

she said. "I can see it all."

She pointed to Aleck. "You are going overseas to win your fortune," she went on. "Great heaps of gold are waiting for you in a foreign land."

Aleck laughed. It sounded very nice, but impossible. How could a boy, not very clever at his lessons, ever make shining heaps of gold in a foreign land?

But how wonderful if would be if he could!

"Maybe you'll see Mr. Barnum's mermaid in New York!" Jim Murray laughed as they walked home together.

Visible Speech

ALECK stayed a whole year in London. His family thought that was long enough. They missed him very much.

All of the family, Sandy and his parents, Mr. and Mrs. McGregor and Mary Ellen and her mother and father were at the station to meet him. He saw them as he raced down the long platform. His big bag bumped against his legs. He waved his cane at them.

But they didn't wave back! They didn't recognize him! They stared right past him.

He rushed up to them, put his bag down and cried, "Doesn't anybody know me?"

Mr. Bell stared at his stylishly dressed son. "It can't be you!" he exclaimed.

Aleck laughed. He had just remembered his London clothes. No wonder they hadn't recognized him!

He took off his tall silk hat. In a minute he looked like the old Aleck. His dark hair stood up the same way all over his head. Grandfather Bell hadn't been able to change that!

"I know you now!" Mrs. Bell laughed. She tried to smooth his rough hair as she had done since he was a little boy.

Milton Cottage seemed small after Grandfather Bell's big London house. But it was in the country and it was "home."

Aleck's father was now teaching his method of helping deaf people speak in the University of Edinburgh. Mrs. Bell was very proud of him.

"Most people," she said, "treat speech defects with magical charms. They think if you put a fork on your tongue, or tubes between your teeth, or pebbles in your mouth, it will help. Your father says that's foolish. He says stammering and stuttering can be cured if a person will learn to speak slowly, breathe right, and place the tongue correctly."

Mr. Bell came home from the college one evening looking very sad. He didn't eat much supper that evening.

"What is the matter?" Mrs. Bell asked.

"A group of men came to visit me today," Mr. Bell explained. "They are against my ways of teaching. They want me to show them something about my Visible Speech. They don't believe what I say is true. They don't believe I can use pictures of sounds to teach people to speak English."

"But we know you can!" Mrs. Bell said. "You have been successful. Look how you and Aleck taught Mary Ellen to speak!"

166

Mr. Bell began to feel better. Mrs. Bell was right. Mary Ellen was a very good example of the success of his method.

"Why don't you invite those men who doubt you to the house?" Mrs. Bell said. "Then get the boys and Mary Ellen to help you. The boys know the pictures, too. Especially Aleck."

"That's a good idea!" Mr. Bell declared. "I'll invite some important scientists, too."

The boys were delighted to help their father. So was Mary Ellen. It would be easy for them to show these gentlemen how Mr. Bell's Visible Speech could be used.

The eventful evening arrived. So did the gentlemen. The boys and Mary Ellen, dressed in their best clothes, shook hands with them. Then the children were sent out of the room.

"Now," said Mr. Bell, "if you will give me some words, I will draw the pictures of the way your throat, tongue and lips look when you are saying the word. My boys and the little girl have learned my set of pictures, just as they would learn their A B C's. From my pictures they will tell you what word you told me to write."

Different words were suggested. The boys and Mary Ellen were called in, one at a time. They recognized the pictures at once and said the words correctly.

Finally one stubborn man said, "Put the pictures of this noise down on your blackboard and see what your sons can do with it!"

He made a long yawning sound, stretching his arms up over his head and twisting his body like a person who is very, very tired. He hoped this would prove that Mr. Bell's method couldn't be used successfully.

Mr. Bell wrote the pictures on the blackboard.

It happened to be Aleck's turn. He studied the pictures for a long time. He had never seen anythink like them. Finally he made the sound of the yawn. Everyone thought it was funny, because he didn't stretch his arms or twist his body at the same time.

The stubborn gentleman had to admit that Aleck was right. He jumped to his feet and clapped his hands. "That was excellent!"

The others all thought Aleck was clever. They thought Mr. Bell's method a great success. They went home convinced that it was good.

When the family were alone they talked of the success of the evening.

"I don't know what I would have done without you boys and Mary Ellen to help me," Mr. Bell said gratefully. He smiled at his sons.

"I have decided," Aleck said thoughtfully, "that I am not going to play the piano when I grow up. I am going to be like you, Father, and teach the deaf to talk."

Mr. Bell smiled happily. It had indeed been a good evening for him.

Boston

Two tall young men walked slowly along Court Street in Boston. One held a slip of paper. He was comparing the number on it with the numbers on the houses. At last he spotted the right number on the other side of the street.

"There it is, Sandy!" James Murray said.

They crossed the street and entered. They stepped into the office of a busy workshop. It seemed cool after the hot June sun outside.

"Is this Mr. Williams' shop?" Sandy Cunningham asked politely.

The man behind the desk nodded. "Yes. What can I do for you?"

"We'd like very much to see Alexander Graham Bell. We heard he was working here. Would you be good enough to tell him that his old friends James Murray and Sandy Cunningham are here?"

"It wouldn't do any good for me to call him," the man said. "Graham wouldn't even hear me." He pointed to the stairs in the hallway. "Go on up. He's in the attic with his friend Tom Watson. They're inventing something. They're so wrapped up in it they can scarcely take time to eat or sleep."

"Thank you," Sandy said. "Come on, Jim."

They ran up the stairs. It had been a long time since they had seen their friend. As he neared the top, James Murray stopped.

"Do you suppose Aleck will remember me?" he asked Sandy.

"I don't see why not," Sandy said stoutly. "You remember him, don't you?"

"I still live in London. The old scenes are familiar to me. There's no reason why I shouldn't remember," James said.

James knew that Aleck had traveled and met many people in the years that had passed since they were last together. He had gone to Canada with his family. Then he had moved to the United States. He had followed in his father's footsteps, and now was a popular teacher in a successful school for the deaf in Boston. He might very well have forgotten London and his old friend James Murray.

"I don't think anything could change Aleck!" Sandy said.

As they reached the top floor a door burst open and a young man dashed out. He was tall and slender. His face was pale, and he had side whiskers and a big mustache. He had a big nose and a high sloping forehead that was crowned by bushy black hair, standing straight on end!

In spite of these changes, the two men knew their old friend at once.

"Aleck!" Sandy shouted happily. "Alexander Graham Bell!"

Aleck dashed right past them as if he did not see Sandy. He ran into the next room, leaving the door open.

They followed him into the room. There wasn't anything else to do.

When they stepped across the threshold they found themselves in an attic room with high, fly-specked windows. It seemed as hot as an oven. The June sun was beating on the roof above. Aleck was leaning over a plain kitchen table on which was a simple-looking machine. Another young man was bending over it, too. They were both too excited to speak. They were certainly too excited to see the strangers.

"Tom," Aleck said slowly, "we've done it! We've sent sound over an electric wire! I heard it in the other room. Tom, this is the beginning of the telephone. Someday you'll hear my voice come over that wire."

James Murray forgot that he was in an attic room in Boston. He forgot that Aleck Bell and he were now men. He remembered the little green park in Harrington Square. He remembered how he and Aleck had walked under the trees and talked about what they were going to do when they grew up. Well, he and his associates were already at work on his Oxford Dictionary. Now Aleck's dream of inventing a machine to carry sound had come true!

"Aleck!" he cried. He went over to the table and put his hand on his friend's shoulder. "Remember me? James Murray? And here's Sandy Cunningham, too!"

Aleck whirled around. His black eyes were snapping with excitement. But he was the same Aleck. He held out his hand in his friendly way.

174

"Jim! Sandy!" he cried. "What a wonderful time to have you arrive! Look! There's the first telephone! Tom and I have been working on it for months. Just a few moments ago, when I was in the other room, I heard a strange sound come over this wire. It's the first sound that has ever been carried by——"

Tom Watson interrupted him. "It was only a faint echo," he told them. "Luckily the right man had his ear to the receiver at the right moment and caught it!"

Sandy Cunningham laughed. "I remember something Aleck's old music teacher used to say to him. 'You have a sensitive ear, my boy. You hear more than most people.' "

For a moment Aleck's face was grave as he remembered his old teacher.

"Poor Signor Bertini! How I disappointed him! He always wanted me to take his place on the concert stage. He was always sure I would."

He paused for a moment, then went on. "I was more interested in my family's work with the deaf. I've been trying to invent a machine that would show deaf children in the Horace Mann school here how vibrations in the air affect our ears as sound. It was a failure, but the machine has become the first telephone instrument you are looking at now. I want people to know that the telephone is a product of the work of the Horace Mann School for the deaf."

"Remember Madam Rockwell's prophecy?" James asked later. He and Aleck and Sandy were having supper together. " 'There will be heaps of shining gold for you in a foreign land'? Of course she probably told everyone something like that, but for you it seems to have come true."

Aleck shook his head.

"There are months of hard work ahead for Tom Watson and me," he told James seriously. "We have to perfect that instrument you saw today. So far we have heard only a sound over it. I want the human voice to come over it as clearly as if the person speaking was in the next room, or standing next to you."

"You'll succeed!" Sandy Cunningham said stoutly. He had great faith in his friend. "Here's a toast for you, Aleck. Here's to the day when you come back to Edinburgh as one of her greatest citizens! They'll give the lads in McLaren's Academy a holiday in your honor."

Recognition

THE year 1876 was the hundredth birthday of the United States. The young nation was very proud of all it had achieved in one century. It had a big birthday party and invited the whole world to Philadelphia to a great exhibition.

The guest of honor was Dom Pedro, the Emperor of Brazil. He came with his Empress and important people from his court. They sailed from Brazil in three of the largest battleships in the Brazilian Navy. The streets of Philadelphia were draped with banners that read, "Welcome, Dom Pedro!"

Everyone visited the Centennial Exhibition

buildings. Countries all over the world had sent exhibits. Bright lights, rich draperies, brilliant colors made the buildings gay.

In one room Aleck stood beside his new invention, the telephone. He hoped someone would take an interest in his instrument and stop to ask how it worked.

His machine was in a dark corner, out of the way, however. All day long he watched a stream of people pass. They never turned to glance at the young inventor and his machine. Aleck had thought he would have to answer many questions, but no one was curious.

The long dreary day drew to a close. Aleck was tired and hungry. He would have given anything for one of the mutton pies he used to buy in Edinburgh. How good one of them would taste now!

He wished he could leave the Exhibition, and go back to Boston. He threw a black cloth over his machine and turned to get his hat and coat. There was no reason to stay longer tonight. It was almost seven o'clock.

Then he saw several men coming toward him. At last the judges were coming to see his invention! His heart lifted. He swept off the cloth and patted his beloved machine.

One of the judges said, "We are sorry to be late, Mr. Bell, but there are so many, many interesting exhibits——"

Aleck's spirits sank. The man must mean there were many exhibits more interesting than his. He answered two or three questions, but he was shy. He had lost faith in himself and his telephone. Some of the men yawned politely behind their hands and glanced at their watches. "Bell's telephone is interesting as gadgets go," they thought. "But it can never be more than a passing fad."

Then the door of the hall opened. A tall man

with blond hair and a beard swept in. Immediately the room seemed to light up. Aleck's spirits soared again as the gentleman hurried toward him. The judges watched in amazement.

"My young friend, Alexander Graham Bell!" the stranger cried. "How glad I am to see you again! How goes the school for the deaf in Boston, where you were teaching the last time I saw you? What are you doing here in Philadelphia, so far from home?"

"Thank you for your kind interest, Dom Pedro," Aleck said humbly. "I have come here to exhibit a new invention of mine. I call it a telephone. The human voice is carried over this wire." He began to show Dom Pedro, the Emperor of Brazil, how his machine worked.

"Very interesting!" Dom Pedro cried. "I must try it! Show me what I am to do."

"Just put this receiver to your ear," Aleck told him. "I'll go to another part of the building and talk to you. You will hear my voice coming over the wire."

Dom Pedro held the receiver gingerly. It seemed impossible that this could be true. How could a human voice come through five hundred feet of electrified wire? But he knew Aleck was a clever young man. The Emperor had been interested in the school in Boston where Aleck taught. He liked the young Scotsman.

Aleck, in another part of the building, stood by the mouthpiece of the telephone. In a moment he would speak over his invention to the Emperor. But he couldn't think of anything to say! His mind seemed a perfect blank. Then suddenly he remembered his grandfather. Mr. Bell used to read aloud from a book of plays by William Shakespeare. Aleck remembered: "To be or not to be, that is the question——" He recited the whole of it.

Dom Pedro almost dropped the receiver!

Aleck was speaking directly into his ear! He had watched the young inventor leave the room. Yet his voice sounded as though he were beside him. He could hardly believe it.

"It speaks!" the Emperor shouted.

The judges forgot they were tired. They crowded around. They wanted to hear, too. They forgot their good manners, and pushed and shoved like a group of schoolboys. They were delighted when they heard Aleck's voice coming over the wire.

"It speaks!" they all shouted.

Crowds came from other parts of the building to see what all the shouting was about. When they heard what was happening, they wanted to listen, too. Then they grew excited when they heard Aleck's voice coming over the wire.

From that time on the telephone was the most important thing to see and hear at the Exhibition. Aleck Bell's invention was a success.

New Dreams

ALECK sat in a room of the Telephone Building in New York City on January 25, 1915. He was about to talk to his friend Tom Watson, who was in California. It seemed to Aleck the most important moment in his life.

Ever since that long-ago night when he and Sandy Cunningham had been lost and kind Mr. and Mrs. McGregor had taken them in, he had thought about inventing a machine to make it possible for people to speak to those they loved across miles and miles of land. He had never forgotten how he would have liked to hear his mother's soft voice that night. Now his dream

186

had come true! Thirty-four hundred miles away Tom Watson waited to speak to him.

Aleck waited for the bell to ring that would tell him Tom was ready to talk. He thought of all the things that had happened since that hot June afternoon when James Murray and Sandy had hurried up the stairs of 109 Court Street in Boston, just in time to celebrate the invention of the telephone. How hard and long he and Tom Watson had worked over that first crude instrument. How much had happened since then!

He smiled to himself as he remembered his interview with Queen Victoria of England. She had not remembered the little boy who had once picked up her fan on Princes Street in Edinburgh. He had not dared to remind her.

When Queen Victoria had become interested in the telephone she had sent for Aleck. She wanted to see how the telephone worked. When Aleck came in, he had scarcely recognized the tiny, stout, old lady seated in a big chair. Only her voice seemed the same.

However, the tall, gray-haired Scotch soldier who stood at attention behind her hadn't changed much. It was Jamie Dunlop. Jamie Dunlop of Shinbone Alley, a special guardian of the Queen! His dark eyes had snapped and twinkled when Alexander Graham Bell was announced, but he hadn't turned a hair. He had stood at attention during the interview.

Aleck had been told how to conduct himself before the Queen. But he was excited and a little nervous about the success of his telephone, and he forgot. The Queen was missing the very best part of his exhibition. She wasn't holding the receiver close enough to her ear. Aleck forgot what he had been told to do. He leaned forward and touched the Queen's arm and whispered, "Hold it closer!"

There had been a dead silence. Aleck remembered the advice then, too late. He felt his face grow hot as he snatched his hand away. He didn't know what to do. He wasn't supposed to speak to the Queen without being spoken to first. He couldn't apologize.

Queen Victoria had calmly ignored the whole thing, however. She had pressed the receiver closer to her ear and smiled her thanks.

Now someone entered the room in New York where Aleck sat waiting for the signal. The man laid a paper on the desk before Aleck.

"We thought it might be easier if we wrote something for you to say," he said.

Aleck took the paper, glanced at it and tossed it to one side.

"I know what I'm going to say to Tom," he said with a smile.

He did, too. He was going to say exactly what he had said that first time Tom had heard his voice over the telephone.

Tom had been in another room in the same house. Aleck had suddenly spilled acid on his clothing. It had burned right through the cloth. He had been startled and rather afraid. "Mr. Watson, come here. I want you!" he had called.

Faithful Tom had rushed into the room. "I heard every word you said, Mr. Bell!" he had shouted. "I heard everything—clearly."

Aleck chuckled. Tom would enjoy this.

He pulled a piece of paper toward him and began to draw a small bell. That had indeed become his "trade-mark." It was now placed outside every store and public building that had one of his telephones in it. A bell for his name!

The phone rang and Aleck picked up the receiver. Tom Watson's voice came over, clear and strong, across the miles of wire. "Hello!" he called. "Hello, Graham, are you there?"

Aleck grinned like a mischievous schoolboy. "Mr. Watson, come here. I want you!" he cried.

He glanced at the paper he had tossed aside on his desk. The people outside must have wanted him to say something flowery. But Tom Watson had understood and enjoyed that first message. His hearty laugh rang in Aleck's ear.

"I'd be glad to, Graham, but it would take me a week this time!" he said.

"Then we'll have to think of a quicker way to get you here," Aleck answered.

He was thinking of airplanes, in which he and several friends were now interested.

"Very well!" Tom answered. "You tell me how, and I'll try and make it for you!"

They spoke a few more words. Then the connection was broken. Aleck hung up the receiver.

He sat at his desk for a long moment before he answered the knock on his door. Crowds of people were waiting outside to congratulate him. It was the first coast-to-coast telephone call.

Now that one plan was finished, he wanted to

begin another. Now that mothers and children, friends and acquaintances, husbands and wives, were able to speak to one another across miles of space, he wanted to think of a way that would bring them to one another. A way quicker than trains, quicker than automobiles. He wanted to bring them together as fast as a bird could fly—even faster!

More About This Book

WHEN ALEXANDER GRAHAM BELL LIVED

1847   ALEXANDER BELL WAS BORN IN EDINBURGH, SCOTLAND, MARCH 3.

There were twenty-nine states in the Union.

James K. Polk was President.

The population of the country was about 23,191,000.

1848–   ALECK STARTED TO GROW UP AND TOOK ON THE
1861   MIDDLE NAME GRAHAM.

Gold was discovered in California, 1848.

First message was sent across the Atlantic Ocean by cable, 1858.

Abraham Lincoln was President, 1861-1865.

The War between the States began, 1861.

1862–   ALECK WORKED AS A SPEECH TEACHER WITH
1870   HIS FATHER IN EDINBURGH AND LONDON.

Lincoln delivered a famous address at Gettysburg, 1863.

President Lincoln was assassinated, 1865.

The first permanently successful transatlantic cable was laid, 1866.

The United States purchased Alaska, 1867.

The first transcontinental railroad was completed, 1869.

1870   ALECK BELL MOVED TO AMERICA AND BEGAN TO BUILD A TELEPHONE.

The United States Weather Bureau was established, 1870.

Ulysses S. Grant was President, 1869-1877.

1876   ALEXANDER GRAHAM BELL EXHIBITED HIS FIRST WORKABLE TELEPHONE.

Rutherford B. Hayes was President, 1877-1881.

Bicycles were first made in this country, 1878.

Thomas Edison invented the phonograph, 1878, and the electric light bulb, 1879.

1880–   BELL WORKED ON MANY INVENTIONS AND CAR-
1921   RIED ON MANY EXPERIMENTS.

Thomas A. Edison invented the moving-picture camera, 1889.

Wilbur and Orville Wright flew the first heavier-than-air aircraft, 1903.

World War I was fought, 1914-1918.

194

1922 ALEXANDER GRAHAM BELL DIED, AUGUST 2.

There were forty-eight states in the Union.

Warren G. Harding was President.

The population of the country was about 139,840,000.

DO YOU REMEMBER?

1. Why did Aleck and Melville have a fight on their way through Shinbone Alley?

2. What birthday gift did Aleck have from his Grandfather Bell?

3. What happened when Aleck and Sandy rode into the country with a farmer?

4. How did Aleck come to take on the middle name, Graham?

5. How did Aleck discover that the baby robins on the McGregor farm had hatched?

6. Why was Mrs. Bell luckier than many people who started to lose their hearing?

7. How did Aleck warn everybody that the school building was on fire?

8. How did Aleck get an opportunity to talk with Queen Victoria?

9. What special trick did Aleck teach his new dog Terry?

10. What kind of talking machine did Aleck and Melville make, and what could it say?

11. What took place during the birthday party for Aleck and Grandfather Bell?

12. What kind of new suit did Grandfather Bell get for Aleck?

13. How did Aleck, Melville, and Mary Ellen help to demonstrate Mr. Bell's Visible Speech?

14. What did Alexander Graham Bell start to do after he came to Boston?

15. Where did Bell first exhibit his telephone?

16. What happened when Bell demonstrated his telephone to Queen Victoria?

IT'S FUN TO LOOK UP THESE THINGS

1. Where is Scotland and to what large country does it belong?

2. What are the people of Scotland called?

3. What is the game cricket which is mentioned in the story?

4. Who was Phineas T. Barnum and how did he become famous?

5. How does a fortune teller work and pretend to look at the future?

6. Why did Alexander Graham Bell decide to come to America?

7. What other things besides the telephone did Bell develop or invent?

INTERESTING THINGS YOU CAN DO

1. Collect pictures of Scotland and help to prepare an exhibit of Scottish scenes on the bulletin board.

2. Read about Tom Thumb, who Aleck saw in London, and give a report to the class.

3. Make a drawing to show what you think a telephone is like and how it works.

4. Find out more about the Centennial Exhibition which was held in Philadelphia. Where have other fairs been held since that time?

5. Make a list of famous men besides Bell who have invented ways of communicating by long distance and tell what each has done.

OTHER BOOKS YOU MAY ENJOY READING

Boys' Book of Communication, Raymond F. Yates. Harper.

Great Men of Scotland, Theo Lang. Roy Publishing Co.

Let's Go to the Telephone Company, Naomi Buchheimer. Putnam.

Mr. Bell Invents the Telephone, Katherine B. Shippen. Trade Edition, Random House. School Edition, Hale.

Scottish Chiefs, Jane Porter. Scribner.

Tales of Scottish Keeps and Castles, Elizabeth W. Grierson. Macmillan.

Tom Edison: Boy Inventor, Sue Guthridge. Trade and School Editions, Bobbs-Merrill.

INTERESTING WORDS IN THIS BOOK

bagpipes (băg'pīps') : musical instruments made of a mouthpiece, bag, and several pipes

bellows (bĕl'ōz) : device for pumping or blowing air

chandelier (shăn'dĕ lēr') : light fixture hanging from a ceiling

chestnut (chĕs′nŭt) : reddish-brown

chintz (chĭnts) : kind of printed cloth

christening (krĭs′ĕn ĭng) : ceremony of baptizing or naming a child

cobblestoned (cŏb′ ′l stōn′d′) : paved with small rounded stones

compartment (kŏm pärt′mĕnt) : small room or other enclosed place

corridor (kŏr′ĭ dôr) : hallway

crescent (krĕs′ĕnt) : curved like the new moon

cricket (krĭk′ĕt) : game played with a ball and bat, somewhat like baseball

crook (kroŏk) : shepherd's staff

discords (dĭs′kôrdz) : unpleasant combinations of musical sounds

dissected (dĭ sĕk′tĭd) : cut apart

earl (ûrl) : British nobleman

Eton jacket (ē′t'n jăk′ĕt) : short coat worn by students at Eton, an English boys' school

gorge (gôrj) : deep narrow valley or ravine

gutta-percha (gŭt′ȧ-pûr′chȧ) : substance, somewhat like rubber, obtained from a tree

highboy (hī′boi′) : tall chest of drawers on legs

kilts (kĭlts) : short skirt-like garment worn by men in Scotland

miniature (mĭn′ĭ a̍ tu̇r) : very small painting

muck (mŭk) : dirt, mud

pewter (pū′tĕr) : mixture of copper and tin used in making dishes and other tableware

plaid (plăd) : cotton or woolen cloth woven in a pattern of checks and stripes

porridge (pŏr′ĭj) : cereal, such as oats, cooked in water or milk

sensitive (sĕn′sĭ tĭv) : quick to notice things

signor (sē′nyȯr) : Italian word for mister

skirling (skûrl′ĭng) : giving off a shrill sound

Stuart (stū′ĕrt) : Scottish family that once ruled Scotland and England

tam-o'-shanter (tăm′ŏ-shăn′tĕr) : round flat cap with a tassel, popular in Scotland

tartan (tär′tăn) : woolen cloth woven in stripes and checks, like a plaid

temptation (tĕmp tā shŭn) : something that invites action or participation

vibrations (vī brā′shŭnz) : back and forth movements

wee (wē) : very small, tiny

ALECK BELL
Ingenious Boy

Aleck Bell was born in Edinburgh, Scotland, in 1847. He lived in a flat with his father and mother and two brothers. His best friend Sandy Cunningham lived in a near-by flat in the same building.

As a boy, Aleck found Edinburgh an exciting place to live. There were castles nestled in the surrounding hills, where kings and queens once had lived. There was Shinbone Alley, where many thugs and thieves operated. There was Princes Street, where nearly everyone came to buy things for their homes.

Often Aleck and Sandy sauntered along Princes Street, admiring things in the windows. Occasionally they went to Shinbone Alley, where Aleck once had a fight with a thug over a package of candles. Now and then Aleck visited friends in the country and finally the family moved to the country. One year Aleck spent the winter with his Grandfather Bell in London.

Both Aleck's father and grandfather were speech teachers. Aleck's father was particularly interested in teaching deaf persons to speak. He even devised special pictures to show deaf persons how to pronounce words that they couldn't hear.